MINIBOOKS FOR YOUNG LEARNERS

Jane Myles

COPYKIT ENGLISH

This is a minibook about
The Body

by ....

This is a minibook about
The Family

by ....

This is a minibook about
me

by ....

This is a minibook about
Hobbies

by ....

north star
ENGLISH LANGUAGE TEACHING

north ★ star
ENGLISH LANGUAGE TEACHING

Minibooks for Young Learners
By Jane Myles

Published by North Star ELT
5 Leverndale Court, Crookston
Glasgow G53 7SJ Scotland
United Kingdom
www.northstarelt.co.uk

Publisher: Andy Cowle
Editorial services: May Corfield
Cover/Interior design: April, www.studio-april.com
Illustrations: Kathrin Jacobsen
Printed by: M & A Thomson Litho Ltd

Based on the concept of a publication originally
entitled *Crazy Pictures*, published
by Mary Glasgow Magazines/Scholastic and
written by Jane Myles.

ISBN: 978-1-907584-02-2

A catalogue record of this book is available from
the British Library.

CONTENTS

INTRODUCTION

About This Book

This book contains 15 photocopiable minibooks which give younger learners a fun and meaningful way to practise the language of everyday life.

They are aimed at young beginners (8- to 11-year-olds) and are intended to give young learners an opportunity to develop basic vocabulary through the medium of simple interactive activities and games. Each book will reflect its owner's personality, as there are various ways of personalising each book (giving personal information, colouring, writing about oneself, one's family and friends, etc). Their small size means that it is easy for students to create their very own books, giving them a real sense of achievement. The multi-activity nature of the minibooks means that each student can work at his or her own pace. There is slightly more length and variety of text in the later minibooks than in the early ones, which provides the possibility of language progression.

Teacher's Notes

The answers to all the missing text and puzzles are in Teacher's Notes that precede each reproducible Minibook. There is also photocopiable background information and some extra teaching suggestions for additional craft or music projects connected with these topics.

Making the Minibooks

The first stage is to photocopy the minibook you have chosen to use. You will need to make double-sided copies to do this. If you have access to a photocopier which automatically does this, either remove the pages from the book or make a double-sided template first. If not, make sure that the reverse side of each page is identical to how it appears in the book.

When putting the books together, make sure that page 2 of each minibook appears directly behind the title page.

The minibooks are easy to construct as long as students follow the instructions carefully about where they should fold the pages and where they should cut the pages.

Check that everyone has folded their minibook down correctly before they do the cutting, as well as before you or they staple the minibook at the spine. However, you may wish to pre-assemble the minibooks ahead of time. This means that the students will focus their attention on content rather than on construction.

Creating a mini-library

Gradually your class will build up a mini-library of minibooks. You can choose from a variety of ways for storing them. One of the best is a shoe-box (i.e., a box which you receive from a shoe shop when you buy new shoes). You may want to also put in dividers in the shoe-box so that the minibooks are divided into different topics and are then easy to find.

Get everyone to write their names in the space on page 1 of their minibook, and then they can proceed independently, doing the puzzles and colouring in the pictures, etc.

Follow-up Work

Apart from following the Exploitation Ideas (craft, art, music, etc) that accompany each minibook, students may enjoy making their own minibooks about similar topics related more to their own country and culture. The small size of each book means that students can see that this is a real possibility.

Sharing information

Because children are innately curious, they will be eager to see how their classmates have filled in certain personal sections and this sharing of information should be encouraged, all the better if it is in English.

Teach the following:

What have you got on page two/three/four, etc?
Encourage your students to use this phrase if they are going to ask their partner to share information. Even make it a feature or rule that if they ask correctly in English, then they are allowed to see what their partner has written or drawn.

ANSWERS

Page 4

England – English; France – French; the Netherlands – Dutch; Belgium – Belgian; Spain – Spanish; Germany – German; Italy – Italian; Switzerland – Swiss; Scotland – Scottish; Wales – Welsh; Ireland – Irish; Greece – Greek

Pages 8 & 9

You mix red and yellow to make orange.
You mix blue and yellow to make green.
You mix red and blue to make purple.

Page 11

Explain to the class that people in Britain (and some other countries) often give their houses names. Give the children some possible names for houses to help them with naming their own house, e.g., 'Sea View', 'The Towers', 'Sunny Corner'.

Page 15

g	e	o	g	r	a	p	h	y
y	g	j	n	o	r	f	s	r
m	a	t	h	s	t	r	i	o
n	m	k	l	q	m	e	l	t
a	e	b	p	u	c	n	g	s
s	s	c	s	n	u	c	n	i
t	w	i	e	a	v	h	e	h
i	c	i	d	r	a	m	a	t
c	c	t	r	m	l	b	q	o
s	h	t	a	m	x	i	t	h

EXPLOITATION IDEAS

Nationalities card game

Make a set of cards to play Pelmanism in small groups. In each set of cards there should be 24 cards representing all the countries and nationalities shown on page 4 of the minibook. The cards are shuffled and placed face down and students take it in turns to turn over two cards. If they match (e.g., the Netherlands + Dutch) then they keep the pairs, otherwise they turn them both face down again. The skill is in remembering which cards are where, and it helps to fix the names of the countries and nationalities in their heads. You may need several sets, as students can play in groups of up to four. You may also want to add a few more countries and nationalities, helped by your students who can suggest more countries, so that you can elicit the correct nationality name from the rest of the class.

Mini interviews

Once the students have filled in and coloured the astrology page (page 7) get them to work in pairs. Make sure they understand and can pronounce the words 'sign' and 'symbol' and get them to ask:
When's your birthday?
What's your star sign?
What's the symbol for your star sign?
Is it earth, air, fire or water?
Since the partner will have those answers in front of them, they simply have to use the astrology chart to reply. However, it gives them practice in speaking.

Doing a class survey/art and craft

Get the class to organise a survey to find which star sign has the greatest number of students belonging to it. Once they have the numbers (by getting one student to stand at the front of the class saying: *How many people are Aquarius/Pisces/Aries?* etc, and another student counting the votes), you can show them how to make a bar chart to display on the wall on a long frieze. Different students can do the illustrations for each of the signs and then a little bar with the numbers can go underneath.

Colour game

Once you have worked with the colour wheel on page 8, you can play the colour game. Divide the class into two teams. Two people from each team compete against each other by coming to the front of the class. This is a race game. All students should put a few books and other possessions on their desks so that you have enough colours to work with.

Say: *Find someone in the class with something purple (or green, white, brown, etc).* The first of the two teams to touch that person wins a point for his/her team.

Art project: Whose bedroom?

Ask your students to draw or paint a picture of what they see from their bedroom window and to bring the pictures into class. Each student then comes to the front of the class and describes the view they have shown in the picture. Help them with new words and write them up on the board in English.

Make a note of each set of words as they come up, with the name of that student next to the words. Later, when the presentation has finished, read out the four or five key words describing one of the pictures and see if the class can remember whose bedroom view this relates to.

Name competition

Once students have filled in their favourite names for people, pets and houses on page 11, get them to read them out in turn while one member of the class writes these names on the board. Start with favourite names for girls, for example. Finally, get the class to vote on each name to find out what the most popular names are for each category. You may want to tell the class that as of 2009 the most popular names in the UK were (boys) Jack, Oliver, Harry, (girls) Olivia, Ruby, Grace, (male dogs) Max, Buddy, Rocky, (female dogs) Molly, Bella, Lucy.

Friends

Only do this exercise if you feel it will not offend sensitive members of the class who may, for example, not feature in lists of friends.

Get the students to look at what they have written on page 13 and to learn the text in English. Then, one by one, they can stand up and give a little speech on the subject of "My Friends".

Personality

On page 16 there is a chance for students to list what they think are their best qualities. Let students study the list for a moment and then ask them to decide which is the one most important quality of all on the list. Take a class vote on each adjective to find how many students think it is the most important. Write the adjectives on the board and put the number of votes beside each one to find out what the class thinks as a whole. If the class can come up with some more positive adjectives then of course add them.

If they have quite a lot of vocabulary they can also think up some negative attributes and decide which is the least attractive.

My best friends are called

....

.... and

....

.... is taller than

....

.... is shorter than

....

.... makes me laugh.

.... is my oldest friend.

.... lives nearest to me.

I like to have ☐ a few good friends. ☐ lots of friends.

I'm ....

Match the nationalities to the countries

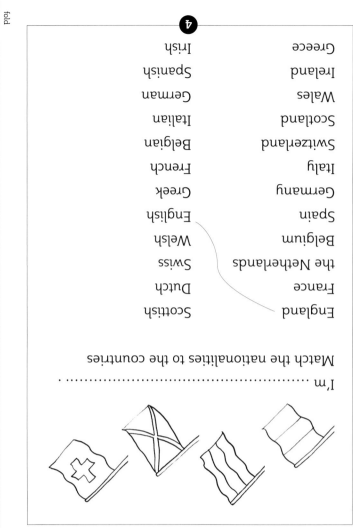

Scottish	England
Dutch	France
Swiss	the Netherlands
Welsh	Belgium
English	Spain
Greek	Germany
Belgian	Italy
French	Switzerland
Italian	Scotland
German	Wales
Spanish	Ireland
Irish	Greece

fold

These words describe my good qualities:

☐ sporty   ☐ friendly

☐ beautiful   ☐ happy

☐ clever   ☐ loyal

☐ cute   ☐ musical

☐ funny   ☐ quiet

                       ☐ strong

© 2010 North Star ELI COPYKIT ENGLISH: Minibooks for Young Learners (ISBN 978-1-907584-02-2) www.northstareli.co.uk

This is a minibook about

me

by ....

FAVOURITE THINGS FAMILY FRIENDS MY ROOM BIRTHDAY

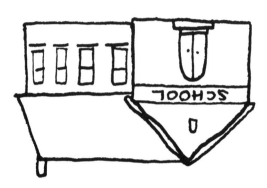

I live in
- [ ] a small village
- [ ] a big town
- [ ] an enormous city

called ....

It's in ....
(e.g. France, Germany, Italy, Spain, Poland, the Netherlands, Finland, Russia, Belgium, Sweden, Norway, Denmark, Russia, etc)

My school is called ....

I'm in .... (class)

My favourite subjects are:

....

....

....

My English teacher is called

....

I'm .... years old.

My birthday is on ....

JANUARY

M	T	W	T	F	S	S
				01	02	03
04	05	06	07	08	09	10
11	12	13	14	15	16	17
18	19	20	21	22	23	24
25	26	27	28	29	30	31

FEBRUARY

M	T	W	T	F	S	S
01	02	03	04	05	06	07
08	09	10	11	12	13	14
15	16	17	18	19	20	21
22	23	24	25	26	27	28

MARCH

M	T	W	T	F	S	S
01	02	03	04	05	06	07
08	09	10	11	12	13	14
15	16	17	18	19	20	21
22	23	24	25	26	27	28
29	30	31				

APRIL

M	T	W	T	F	S	S
			01	02	03	04
05	06	07	08	09	10	11
12	13	14	15	16	17	18
19	20	21	22	23	24	25
26	27	28	29	30		

MAY

M	T	W	T	F	S	S
				01	02	03
04	05	06	07	08	09	10
11	12	13	14	15	16	17
18	19	20	21	22	23	24
25	26	27	28	29	30	31

JUNE

M	T	W	T	F	S	S
01	02	03	04	05	06	07
08	09	10	11	12	13	14
15	16	17	18	19	20	21
22	23	24	25	26	27	28
29	30					

JULY

M	T	W	T	F	S	S
		01	02	03	04	05
06	07	08	09	10	11	12
13	14	15	16	17	18	19
20	21	22	23	24	25	26
27	28	29	30	31		

AUGUST

M	T	W	T	F	S	S
					01	02
03	04	05	06	07	08	09
10	11	12	13	14	15	16
17	18	19	20	21	22	23
24	25	26	27	28	29	30

SEPTEMBER

M	T	W	T	F	S	S
01	02	03	04	05	06	07
08	09	10	11	12	13	14
15	16	17	18	19	20	21
22	23	24	25	26	27	28
29	30					

OCTOBER

M	T	W	T	F	S	S
			01	02	03	04
05	06	07	08	09	10	11
12	13	14	15	16	17	18
19	20	21	22	23	24	25
26	27	28	29	30		

NOVEMBER

M	T	W	T	F	S	S
					01	02
03	04	05	06	07	08	09
10	11	12	13	14	15	16
17	18	19	20	21	22	23
24	25	26	27	28	29	30
31						

DECEMBER

M	T	W	T	F	S	S
					01	02
05	06	07	08	09	10	11
12	13	14	15	16	17	18
19	20	21	22	23	24	25
26	27	28	29	30		

Find the following subjects in the wordsearch below:

history, drama, music, geography, French, gymnastics, maths, science, English, games, art, IT*

(*IT = information technology = computers)

g	e	o	g	r	a	p	h	y
y	g	j	n	o	r	f	s	r
m	a	t	h	s	t	r	i	o
n	m	k	l	q	m	e	l	t
a	e	b	p	u	c	n	g	s
s	s	c	s	n	u	c	n	i
t	w	i	e	a	v	h	e	h
i	c	i	d	r	a	m	a	t
c	c	t	r	m	l	b	q	o
s	h	t	a	m	x	i	t	h

My favourite colour is ....

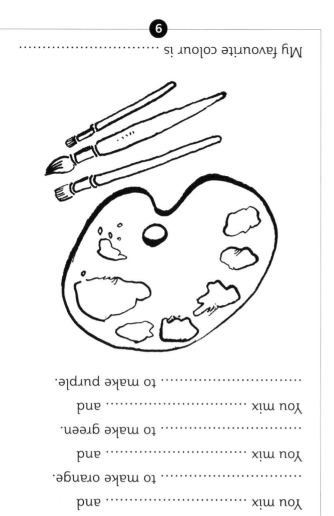

You mix .... and .... to make purple.

You mix .... and .... to make green.

You mix .... and .... to make orange.

Colour the wheel:

Colour wheel segments: purple, orange, blue, white, green, black, yellow, red, pink, cream, dark blue, grey, turquoise, brown

---

☐ I get pocket money every week.

☐ I don't get pocket money.

☐ I earn .... a week because I have a job.

☐ I like to save my money.

☐ I always spend my money.

☐ The most money I have saved is ....
I am saving my money to buy

....

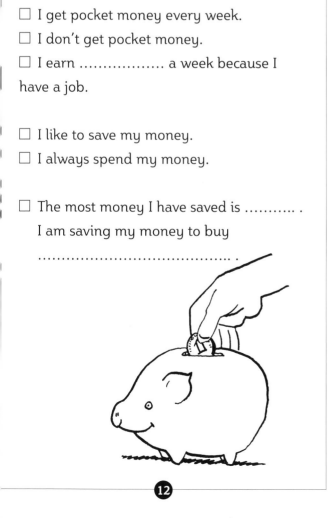

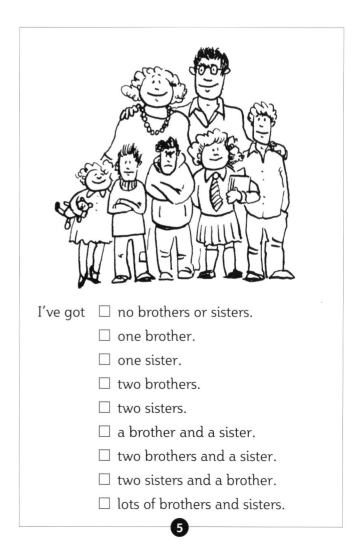

I've got ☐ no brothers or sisters.

☐ one brother.

☐ one sister.

☐ two brothers.

☐ two sisters.

☐ a brother and a sister.

☐ two brothers and a sister.

☐ two sisters and a brother.

☐ lots of brothers and sisters.

fold

My star sign is ....

Cancer Water 22 June–22 July	Capricorn Earth 22 December – 19 January
Gemini Air 22 May–21 June	Sagittarius Fire 22 November–21 December
Taurus Earth 21 April–21 May	Scorpio Water 23 October–21 November
Aries Fire 21 March–20 April	Libra Air 22 September–22 October
Pisces Water 20 February–20 March	Virgo Earth 23 August–21 September
Aquarius Air 21 January–19 February	Leo Fire 23 July–22 August

Colour the signs: water – blue, fire – red,
air – yellow, earth – orange

cut

(books/posters/toys/clothes/guitar, etc)

....

my .... and my ....

my ....

My favourite things in my bedroom are:

□ fields and trees.

□ the sea.

□ our garden.

□ houses or flats.

The bedroom looks out onto

□ I share my bedroom.

□ I've got my own room.

I've got a pet called ....

He/She is a ....
(dog, cat, horse, hamster, canary, snake,
guinea pig, rabbit, parrot, tortoise)

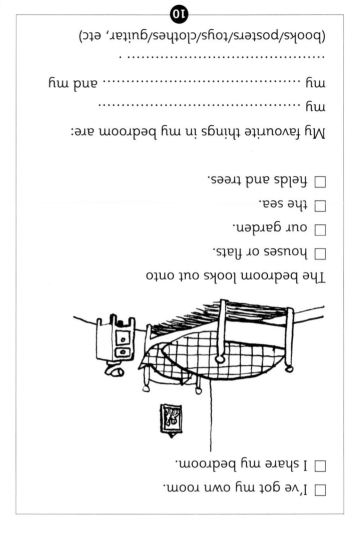

My favourite girl's name is ....
My favourite boy's name is ....
My favourite name for a dog is ....
My favourite name for a cat is ....

When I am older I am going to call my home

....

ANSWERS

Page 4
Please note that your students need to stick a family photo on this page.

Page 13

g	r	a	n	d	f	a	t	h	e	r
a	b	u	c	d	e	n	r	f	e	e
g	u	n	c	l	e	o	e	h	i	h
m	o	t	h	e	r	s	t	h	j	t
n	i	s	u	o	c	o	s	k	l	a
m	n	o	p	q	r	r	i	s	t	f
u	y	b	a	b	v	w	s	x	y	z
d	a	u	g	h	t	e	r	a	b	c

Page 14
1 The First Lady; 2 William; 3 Romeo; 4 Homer; 5 Dursley; 6 two ugly sisters

EXPLOITATION IDEAS

'My family and I': talking about yourself
Ask students to bring a photo of themselves as babies into class. Using the completed text on pages 3, 5, 6, 7, 12 and 16 of their minibooks they can come to the front of the class one by one, put a photo of themselves on the board, and then give a short talk entitled "Let me tell you about myself". They simply use the framework of the text with the filled in gaps and say it aloud having learned it by heart. If they can add extra information to that given on page 2, even better.

Family trees
Who can go back furthest with a family tree in the class? Ask for volunteers to come and draw their tree, naming parents, grandparents, great grandparents (and more if they can!) by Christian name.

Comparatives and superlatives
Page 6 of the minibook contains examples of *oldest* and *youngest*. Check that students know the comparatives as well by chatting about brothers and sisters (*Have you got a brother? Is he older or younger than you?* etc). Use this to practise other comparatives and superlatives of more common adjectives, making sure that there a few irregular ones such as *good, better, best; bad, worse, worst* and longer words using *more* and *most* (e.g., *beautiful, interesting*, etc). There are some more superlatives on page 16. Use the questions on page 16 to discuss the class superlative awards. Instead of the words 'in my family', use 'in this class' and get students to nominate possible award winners. The class can then vote and there can be a mini Oscar ceremony with the answers in sealed envelopes to be read out by various class members.

Look-alike contest
Referring to page 5 of the minibooks, find out who everyone in class thinks they look like and then try to discover if the class thinks they have anyone who looks like someone famous.

Family quiz

Once your students have completed the quiz on pages 14 and 15 and know the answers, see if any of them can think of a new extra question to ask the class. Check that the English is correct and then perhaps you can use this new extended quiz with another English class in school.

Extra information

Here is an extra fact relating to page 6. Many psychologists have said that the most disadvantageous position in any family is to be the third of four children of the same sex. You are not the oldest, nor are you the baby.

Find the family words in the wordsearch:
baby, daughter, son, father, sister, brother, cousin, mother, grandfather, uncle, aunt

d	a	b	r	e	t	h	g	u	a	d
n	u	q	b	v	w	s	x	y	a	z
m	u	o	d	b	r	i	r	s	t	f
n	a	l	k	s	o	c	u	s	i	n
f	o	m	t	h	e	r	s	t	i	j
t	g	h	o	e	l	c	n	u	h	h
e	e	f	r	n	e	d	c	u	b	a
r	g	d	n	a	f	n	u	b	t	a

In this small family photo you can see my mum/dad/brothers/sisters/grandparents.

Family awards

The loudest person in
my family is my ....

The strongest person in my family is my
....

The kindest person in my family is my
....

The funniest person in my family is my
....

The happiest person in my family is my
....

The cleverest person in my family is my
....

This is a minibook about
The Family
by ....

When I was born, I had ☐ no hair.
☐ some brown hair.
☐ some blond hair.
☐ some black hair.
☐ lots of hair.

I was born ☐ at home.
☐ in hospital.

My first word was

....

When I was born I weighed .... kg.

Famous families

1. In America, the President's wife is called
   ☐ the Top Lady.
   ☐ the Big Lady.
   ☐ the First Lady.

2. The name of Prince Charles' oldest son is
   ☐ Harry.
   ☐ William.
   ☐ Philip.

3. The name of David Beckham's youngest son is
   ☐ Romeo.
   ☐ Ronald.
   ☐ Rocky.

---

cut ✂

This is a picture of me as a baby.

---

4. The name of Bart Simpson's father is
   ☐ Alfred.
   ☐ Homer.
   ☐ Horace.

5. The surname of Harry Potter's aunt and uncle is
   ☐ Weasley.
   ☐ Potter.
   ☐ Dursley.

6. Cinderella has
   ☐ a cruel stepmother.
   ☐ two ugly sisters.
   ☐ a kind grandmother.

fold

.... and ....
(grandparents)

|

This is my family tree:

.... and ....
(grandparents)

|

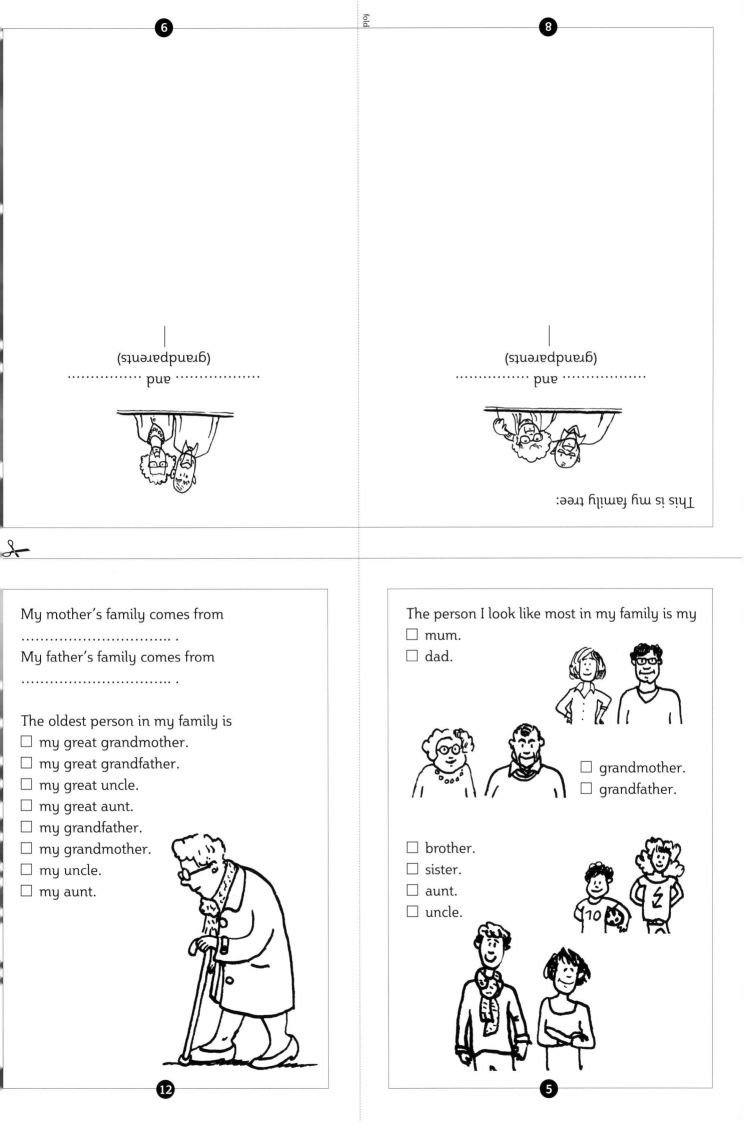

My mother's family comes from
....
My father's family comes from
....

The oldest person in my family is
☐ my great grandmother.
☐ my great grandfather.
☐ my great uncle.
☐ my great aunt.
☐ my grandfather.
☐ my grandmother.
☐ my uncle.
☐ my aunt.

The person I look like most in my family is my
☐ mum.
☐ dad.

☐ grandmother.
☐ grandfather.

☐ brother.
☐ sister.
☐ aunt.
☐ uncle.

JANUARY

M	T	W	T	F	S	S
					01	02
03	04	05	06	07	08	09
10	11	12	13	14	15	16
17	18	19	20	21	22	23
24	25	26	27	28	29	30
31						

FEBRUARY

M	T	W	T	F	S	S
	01	02	03	04	05	06
07	08	09	10	11	12	13
14	15	16	17	18	19	20
21	22	23	24	25	26	27
28						

MARCH

M	T	W	T	F	S	S
	01	02	03	04	05	06
07	08	09	10	11	12	13
14	15	16	17	18	19	20
21	22	23	24	25	26	27
28	29	30	31			

APRIL

M	T	W	T	F	S	S
				01	02	03
04	05	06	07	08	09	10
11	12	13	14	15	16	17
18	19	20	21	22	23	24
25	26	27	28	29	30	

MAY

M	T	W	T	F	S	S
						01
02	03	04	05	06	07	08
09	10	11	12	13	14	15
16	17	18	19	20	21	22
23	24	25	26	27	28	29
30	31					

JUNE

M	T	W	T	F	S	S
		01	02	03	04	05
06	07	08	09	10	11	12
13	14	15	16	17	18	19
20	21	22	23	24	25	26
27	28	29	30			

JULY

M	T	W	T	F	S	S
				01	02	03
04	05	06	07	08	09	10
11	12	13	14	15	16	17
18	19	20	21	22	23	24
25	26	27	28	29	30	31

AUGUST

M	T	W	T	F	S	S
01	02	03	04	05	06	07
08	09	10	11	12	13	14
15	16	17	18	19	20	21
22	23	24	25	26	27	28
29	30	31				

SEPTEMBER

M	T	W	T	F	S	S
			01	02	03	04
05	06	07	08	09	10	11
12	13	14	15	16	17	18
19	20	21	22	23	24	25
26	27	28	29	30		

OCTOBER

M	T	W	T	F	S	S
					01	02
03	04	05	06	07	08	09
10	11	12	13	14	15	16
17	18	19	20	21	22	23
24	25	26	27	28	29	30
31						

NOVEMBER

M	T	W	T	F	S	S
	01	02	03	04	05	06
07	08	09	10	11	12	13
14	15	16	17	18	19	20
21	22	23	24	25	26	27
28	29	30				

DECEMBER

M	T	W	T	F	S	S
			01	02	03	04
05	06	07	08	09	10	11
12	13	14	15	16	17	18
19	20	21	22	23	24	25
26	27	28	29	30	31	

In my dream family I'd like to be

□ an only child.
□ an identical twin.
□ the youngest in a small family.
□ the oldest in a small family.
□ the middle child (of three).
□ the oldest in a big family.
□ the 'baby' of a big family.

cut

Look at the calendar on page 11.

Draw a circle round your birthday.

Colour your mother's birthday green.

Colour your father's birthday yellow.

Colour your sister's birthday blue.

Colour your brother's birthday pink.

Colour your grandmother's birthday orange.

Colour your grandfather's birthday brown.

Colour your parents' wedding anniversary red.

fold

I've got
□ one cousin.
□ no/two/three/four/five/six/*etc* cousins.

I usually spend a lot of time with my cousins

□ at their house.

□ at my house.

□ at my grandparents' house.

□ at Christmas time.

□ in the summer holidays.

□ I don't often see my cousins.

ANSWERS

Page 3
Children have got twenty-four teeth.
Adults have got thirty-two teeth.
When you lose a tooth, the tooth fairy takes the tooth and leaves some money.

Page 4
We have got 206 bones in our bodies.
A quarter (¼) of the bones in my body are in my hands and feet.

Page 5
Hair grows fastest in a man's beard.
(NB Explain to the children that they have to stick one hair to the page with sticky tape.)

Page 7
You blink ten to fifteen times a minute.
(NB Explain to the children that they go to alternate letters around the circle following the example. The blank spaces count as well.)

Page 8
I use more muscles to smile than to frown.

Page 9
The strongest muscle in my body is in my mouth. (It's the jaw.)
(NB Explain to your students that our ancestors who lived two million years ago had much stronger jaws. They could easily bite a hard nut such as a walnut or hard seeds which they needed to survive when food was short.)

I use 300 muscles to balance when I stand.

Pages 10 & 11
You lose 680g of skin every year.
Food stays in your stomach for two hours.
You make 1.5 litres of saliva every day.
2 million blood cells die every second.
Your heart beats 70 times a minute.

Page 12
You cough and sneeze when you have a cold.
The word 'cough' rhymes with 'off'.
A cough travels at 100 km per hour.
A sneeze travels at 150 km per hour.
You can't sneeze with your eyes open.

Page 13
You shiver when you are cold and you sweat when you are hot.

Page 16
You have got the same number of bones in your neck as a giraffe. (*A giraffe's bones are bigger.*)
The "funny bone" is the elbow.

EXPLOITATION IDEAS

Song
If your students like singing, the traditional children's song *One Finger, One Thumb* is quite a good action song to practise parts of the body. You can find the words and hear the song sung on the BBC CBEEBIES site on the internet by typing *One finger one thumb CBEEBIES* into the search engine.

Game
The popular game of *Simon Says* is also a good way to practise body parts. Give the class instructions such as *Simon says, 'Touch your nose'*, etc. If you preface the instruction with the words *Simon says…* everyone has to copy you and do it; if you omit the words *Simon says*, anyone who does the action is out of the game.

Body facts
Your students will probably have to make quite a lot of guesses to answer some of the questions in this minibook. This is fine because they will learn the real facts by seeing how many they got right or wrong.

Numbers

Page 4 practises numbers. Write numbers (1–24 if there are 24 students in the class for example) in large letters on pieces of paper and get students to attach them to their chests. Organise them to stand in a circle and then throw a ball into the air and call out a number in English. The person whose number it is should jump forward and catch the ball. If they miss the ball they go out of the circle and sit down.

Broken bones

Has anyone in the class broken a bone? Which one was it? How long did it take to get better again?

Hair, teeth and eyes survey

Get a group of students to organise a survey to count how many people have brown hair, blond hair, etc, and also eye colour. Once they have completed their survey, they can present their results to the class showing them as either a pie chart or a bar chart. Take a vote on how many "milk teeth" (as children's teeth are called in English) children have kept after they have fallen out.

Organise a 'blinking contest' once the children have completed page 7 of the minibook to see who can keep their eyes open longest without blinking.

Pronunciation and spelling

Use the small puzzle on page 12 about the pronunciation to explain the complexity of English pronunciation. Write the following words on the board:

tough, plough, enough, rough, cough. Tell them what the words mean and explain that *tough, enough* and *rough* rhyme with 'stuff', *plough* rhymes with 'now', while *cough* rhymes with 'off'. On the same page there is also *ache* rhyming with 'take' and *sweat* rhyming with 'let'.

There is only one way to learn these and that is to learn them by heart while using every opportunity to listen to proper spoken English. Songs or poems that feature difficult words are also a good way to fix pronunciation in one's head.

Making a wish

Tell the children that on the count of three (in English) they must all pretend to sneeze. Then, get them all to write their wish on a piece of paper.

Classroom Olympics

Once your students have completed pages 14 and 15 of their minibooks, find out who has ticked all the boxes. Set a few more tasks to find the champion, such as seeing who can stand for the longest on one leg with their eyes closed or who can crouch on the ground and straighten one leg in front of them without touching the ground with their hands. All these body exercises will probably make the children giggle and get excited but this is good as they forget that they are actually learning English and will have good associations of fun with 'English lessons'.

Ask your students:

When do we yawn? (Answer: When we are tired) It is often said that people yawn if they see someone else yawning. Try an experiment by asking two students to sit facing one another and ask one to pretend to yawn. Watch to see if the second student finds this infectious and also starts to yawn. Maybe other members of the class (or you yourself!) will yawn simply by thinking about it.

Write it here: ....

What is your wish?

Imagine you sneeze once.

And four – something better!

Three for a kiss

Two for a letter,

Once for a wish,

In England, when you sneeze, people say:

You sweat when you are ....

You shiver when you are ....

☐ hands and feet.

☐ arms and legs.

☐ head.

in my

bones in my body are

A quarter (¼) of the

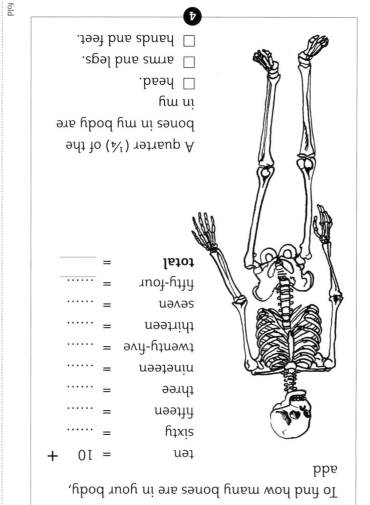

total	=	_____
fifty-four	=	......
seven	=	......
thirteen	=	......
twenty-five	=	......
nineteen	=	......
three	=	......
fifteen	=	......
sixty	=	......
ten	=	10 +

add

To find how many bones are in your body,

1	2	3	4	5	6	7
A	B	C	D	E	F	G

8	9	10	11	12	13	14
H	I	J	K	L	M	N

15	16	17	18	19	20	21
O	P	Q	R	S	T	U

22	23	24	25	26
V	W	X	Y	Z

You have the same number of bones in your neck as a

seven	nine	eighteen	one	six	six	five

English people sometimes call this part of the body their 'funny bone'.

five	twelve	two	fifteen	twenty-three

© 2010 North Star ELT COPYKIT ENGLISH: Minibooks for Young Learners (ISBN 978-1-907584-02-2) www.northstarelt.co.uk

This is a minibook about

The Body

by ....

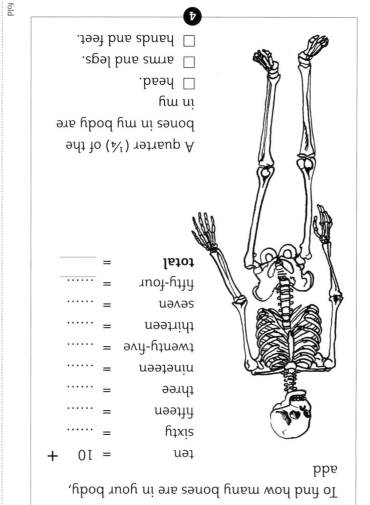

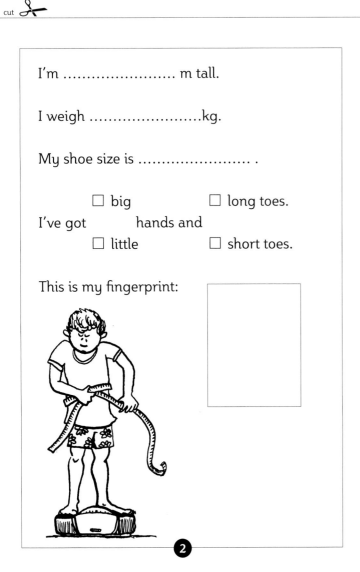

Page 3

When you lose a tooth, ☐ Father Christmas
☐ the tooth fairy
☐ the Easter Bunny
takes the tooth and leaves some money.

I've got .... teeth.

Adults have got ☐ thirty-two teeth.
☐ twenty-four
☐ sixteen

Children have got ☐ sixteen ☐ two teeth.
☐ twenty-four

Page 14

Look what I can do with my body! I can

☐ wink.

☐ dance.

☐ play a musical instrument.

☐ stand on one leg with my eyes closed.

☐ dive.

fold

cut

Page 2

I'm .... m tall.

I weigh ....kg.

My shoe size is ....

☐ big   ☐ long toes.
I've got   hands and
☐ little   ☐ short toes.

This is my fingerprint:

Page 15

☐ swim.

☐ ski.

☐ write with my left hand.

☐ juggle with two balls.

☐ stand on my hands.

☐ wiggle my ears.

Hair

I've got
- [ ] light brown
- [ ] blond
- [ ] black
- [ ] straight
- [ ] curly
- [ ] wavy
- [ ] frizzy
- [ ] dark brown
- [ ] red
- [ ] ginger

hair.

Here is a hair from my head

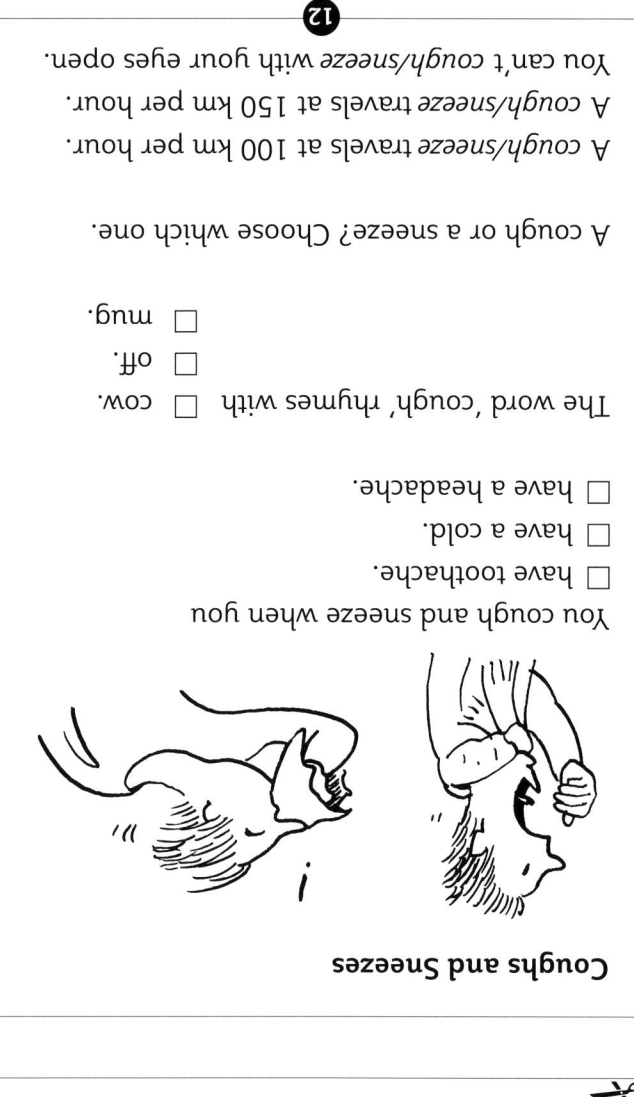

Hair grows fastest
- [ ] on a man's arms.
- [ ] in a man's beard.
- [ ] on a man's head.

5

Coughs and Sneezes

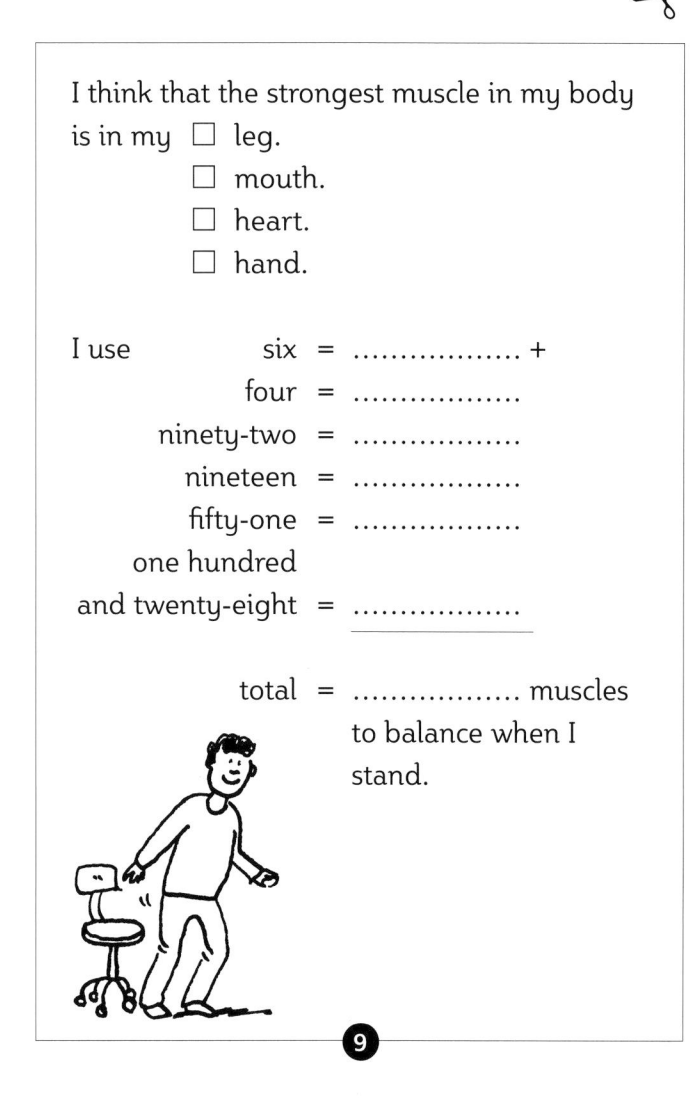

You cough and sneeze when you
- [ ] have toothache.
- [ ] have a cold.
- [ ] have a headache.

The word 'cough' rhymes with
- [ ] cow.
- [ ] off.
- [ ] mug.

A cough or a sneeze? Choose which one.

A cough/sneeze travels at 100 km per hour.

A cough/sneeze travels at 150 km per hour.

You can't cough/sneeze with your eyes open.

12

Muscles

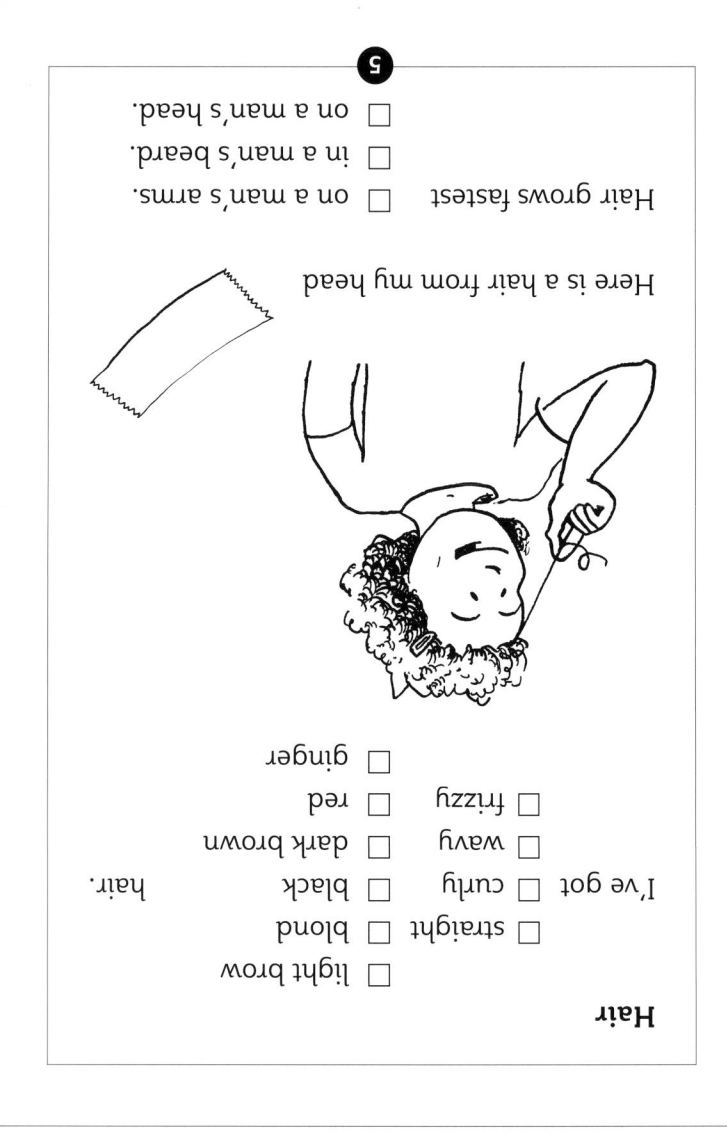

Draw the face

I use more muscles to

Write the numbers as words, for example, 7 = seven

7	[ ]	_ _ _ _
	[ ]	_ _
8	[ ]	_ _ _ _
11	[ ]	_ _ _ _
10	[ ]	_ [ ]_

than to

5	[ ]	_ _ _
3	[ ]	_ _ _ _
1	[ ]	_ _
(cow)	[ ]	_ _ _
9	[ ]	_ _ _

8

I think that the strongest muscle in my body is in my
- [ ] leg.
- [ ] mouth.
- [ ] heart.
- [ ] hand.

I use

six	=	.... +
four	=	....
ninety-two	=	....
nineteen	=	....
fifty-one	=	....
one hundred and twenty-eight	=	....
total	=	.... muscles

to balance when I stand.

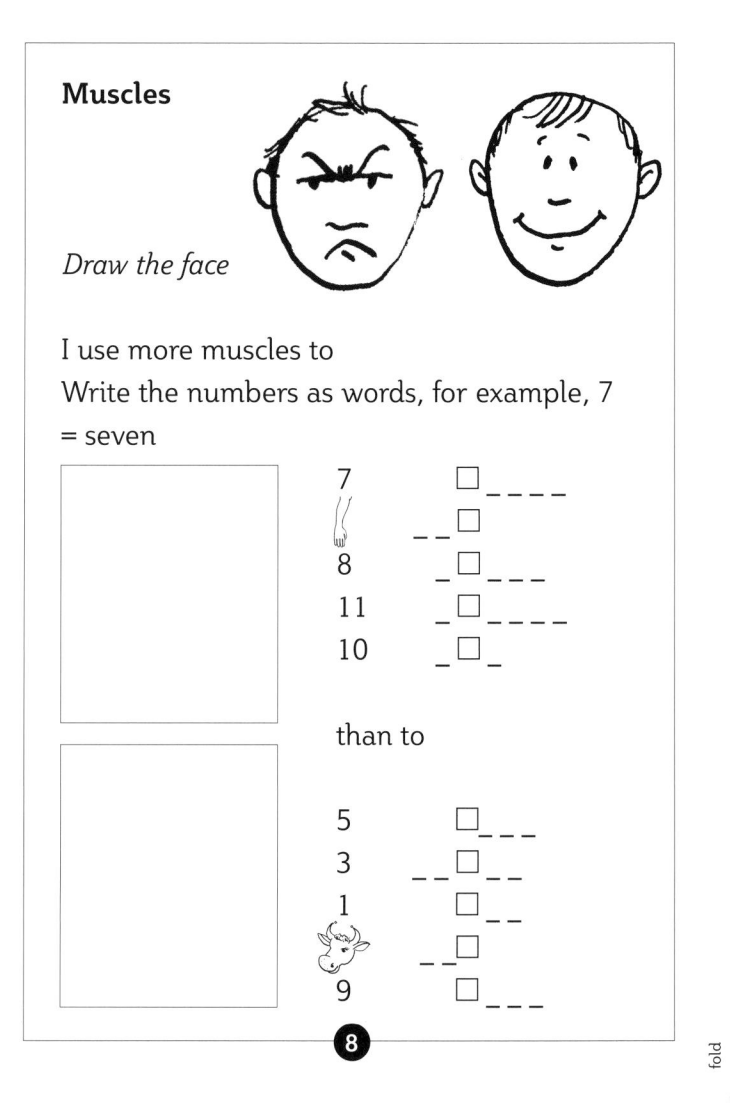

9

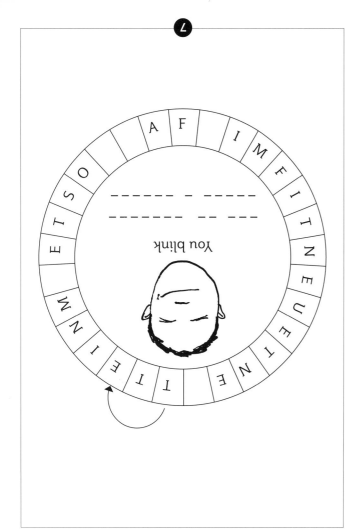

You blink

_ _ _ _ _ _ - _ _ _ _
_ _ _ _ _ _ _ _ - _ _ _

(wheel letters: A F I M F I T N E U E T N E I N E M I I E T I F M T E S O)

Your heart beats …

2 million blood cells …

You make 1.5 litres …

Food stays in your stomach …

You lose 680g of …

Eyes

In my class there are ……………… children.

……………… children have blue eyes.
……………… children have brown eyes.
……………… children have green eyes.
……………… children have hazel eyes.
……………… children have grey eyes.

I've got ……………… eyes.

……………… children in my class wear glasses.

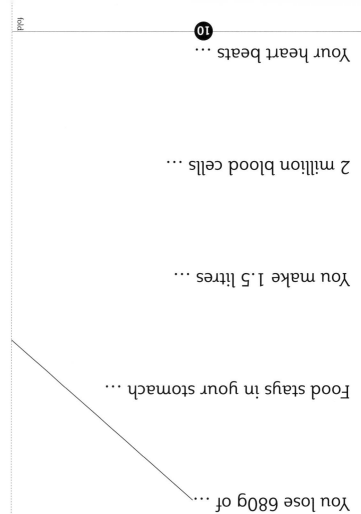

☐ I wear glasses.
☐ I don't wear glasses.

70 times a minute.

of saliva every day.

die every second.

skin every year.

for two hours.

ANSWERS

Pages 4 & 5
Jake's house is House C.

Page 8
It's in the kitchen.

Page 10
1 – e, 2 – a, 3 – c, 4 – b, 5 – g, 6 – f, 7 – d.

Page 12
1 washing machine, 2 shower, 3 saucepan, 4 bath.

Page 14
dog – kennel, parrot – cage, horse – stable, blackbird – nest, tropical fish – aquarium, cat – basket, bee – beehive, rabbit – hutch.

NB a dog could also have a basket as its home; a kennel would be for a dog that lives outside the house. A small aquarium is also called a tank. The word aquarium is also used for the larger building where one can view big fish.

Page 16

a	c	o	m	p	u	t	e	r	w
b	b	r	o	o	f	g	c	i	i
a	e	d	e	f	d	g	h	a	n
t	l	d	o	i	d	a	r	h	d
h	b	i	r	w	a	l	l	c	o
j	a	f	o	s	d	o	o	r	w
k	t	l	m	r	e	w	o	h	s
t	e	l	e	v	i	s	i	o	n

EXPLOITATION IDEAS

Describing your home
Get the children to describe their homes using the same vocabulary as that on page 4 (window, storey, door, chimney, garage, garden). Get them to write these descriptions down and then collect them in and read them out aloud once you have checked the English to see if the class can guess whose house it is. Obviously the owner of the house must stay silent.

What's in your house? Chain questions
Once your students have completed minibook pages 6 & 7, you can hold a general class discussion and vote. Write the names of the rooms across the top of the blackboard and the furniture and objects down the left-hand side. Ask:
How many students have got a table in the hall?
   Count the hands that go up and then write the number in the square under hall and to the right of table. Now student 1 comes to the front and asks the second question:
How many students have got a television in the hall?
   That student counts the votes and writes the result in the square under hall and corresponding to television. That student hands the pen/chalk to the next student. This means that each member of the class will have several turns at asking questions and since the format is very repetitive it's not a difficult task.
   Once the whole grid is filled in, students can see if they can make some statements such as:
In our class 20 children have got a television in the living room.
In our class, 15 children have got a computer in their bedroom, etc.

Craft/modelling game

Hopefully you can obtain a big bag of children's modelling clay for this.

Split the class into several teams – the smaller the better. Have a stopwatch ready and once the whole class counts down from 10 (*Ten, nine, eight…* etc) and reaches *Three, two, one, Go!* the team tries to see how many of the furniture items in the list they can make. Set a time limit, e.g., one minute, and get a student who is not doing the modelling to be the timekeeper and to shout *Stop!* at the end of the minute. Each team gets a point for each item which the class thinks is adequately recognisable. Give a little prize to the winning team. Another student can summarize the results of each heat, e.g., *Maria's team has made a television, a table, a bed*. This is good practice of the household items as once again it is repetitive but the language is being used for a specific purpose, i.e., to count the points.

Hide and seek

Get the students to play a game of virtual 'hide and seek'. Let them look at the list of rooms and items of furniture and objects on pages 6 & 7. You can add a few more such as *wardrobe, cupboard, bath, toilet, bed, sink, oven*, etc, or from the list on page 12. Tell the students to think of a hiding place which must consist of a room in the house and then a position (*under/ behind/next* to), e.g. *in the bedroom, under the bed / in the bedroom, behind the wardrobe*).

Student A comes to the front of the class and the rest of the class asks questions to find out which room he/she is in (*Are you in the kitchen?* etc). Once they have discovered the room, they then ask where the student is in that room (*Are you behind the curtains?* etc). If the class have to ask more than ten questions, Student A has won a point.

Who am I?

This simple game is a very simple filler game for the end of a lesson. Use the list of people in the famous houses on page 11 and secretly assign all of these except one to six chosen players. Assign one name to yourself. They must on no account let anyone know who they are. They come to the front of the class and sit down. They must then try to find out each others' identities. They are not allowed to ask you any questions. Student A asks another student: *John, are you Bart Simpson?*

John must answer simply *Yes, I'm Bart Simpson* or *No, I'm not Bart Simpson*. If he actually is Bart, he drops out of the game and Student A can choose another person to ask. If he is not Bart, he can now address another student and ask *Are you… ?* As before, if he is right, he drops out, but if he is wrong, the person he has asked gets to choose. The skill in this game is for all the players to remember all the characters from which they have to choose. They also have to identify you without asking any questions. They mustn't have their books in front of them or be prompted by the rest of the class. If the game is popular, you can play it with the names of British or American film stars, pop stars or celebrities.

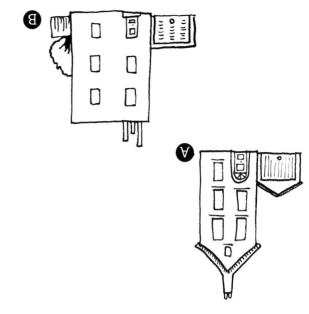

13

4

Which is Jake's house?

It's got three chimneys.
It's a three-storey house.
It's got five windows and a big door.
It's got a garage on the left and a tree in the front garden.

Find 13 things you can see in a house:
computer, window, shower, radio, television, bed, bath, wall, roof, table, chair, door, sofa.

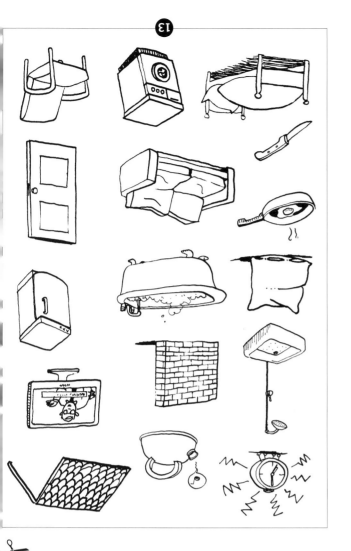

a	c	o	m	p	u	t	e	r	w
b	b	r	o	o	f	g	c	i	i
a	e	d	e	f	d	g	h	a	n
t	l	d	o	i	d	a	r	h	d
h	b	i	r	w	a	l	l	c	o
j	a	f	o	s	d	o	o	r	w
k	t	l	m	r	e	w	o	h	s
t	e	l	e	v	i	s	i	o	n

16

© 2010 North Star ELT COPYKIT ENGLISH: Minibooks for Young Learners (ISBN 978-1-907584-02-2) www.northstarelt.co.uk

This is a minibook about

My Home

My address . . . .

. . . .

. . . .

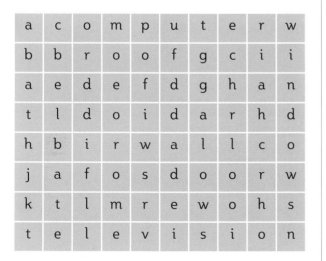

I live ☐ by the sea.
☐ in a village.
☐ in a small town.
☐ in a city.
☐ near a city.
☐ in the countryside.

stable

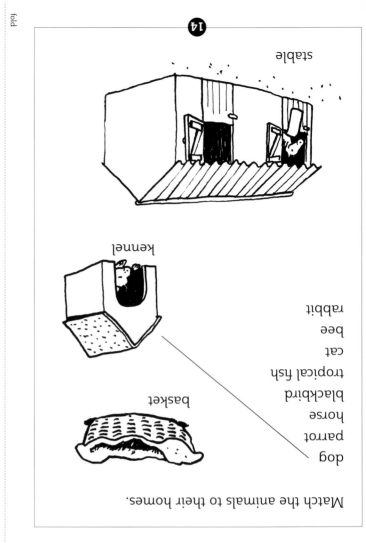

kennel

basket

Match the animals to their homes.

dog
parrot
horse
blackbird
tropical fish
cat
bee
rabbit

My home is a

☐ house.   ☐ castle.
☐ flat.   ☐ cottage.
☐ caravan.   ☐ palace.

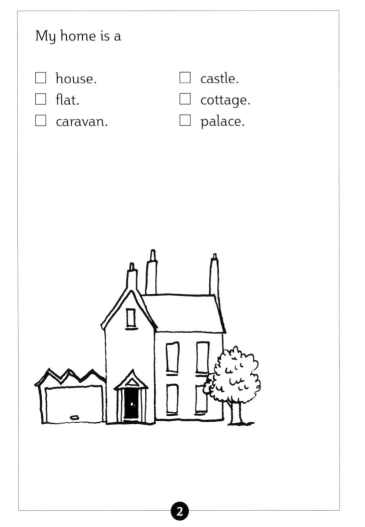

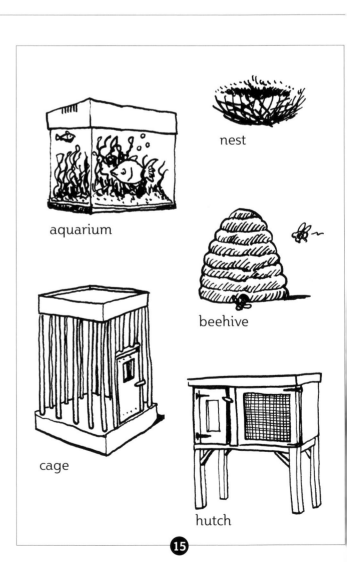

nest

aquarium

beehive

cage

hutch

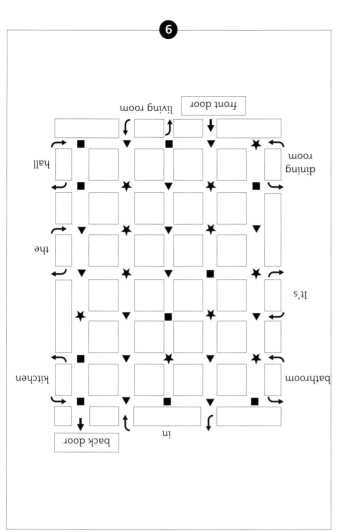

front door | living room

hall

dining room

the

It's

kitchen | bathroom

back door | in

★ = turn left
▼ = go straight on
■ = turn right

....
....
....
....

Write your answer here:

Follow the signs on the map on page 9. Go into the house through the front door.

Help her to find it.
Where is it?

Ruby has lost her mobile phone.

Which is the 'odd one out' in each group?

1. sofa
   television
   armchair
   washing machine

2. shower
   kettle
   knife
   fridge

3. wall
   door
   saucepan
   roof

4. pillow
   bath
   bed
   alarm clock

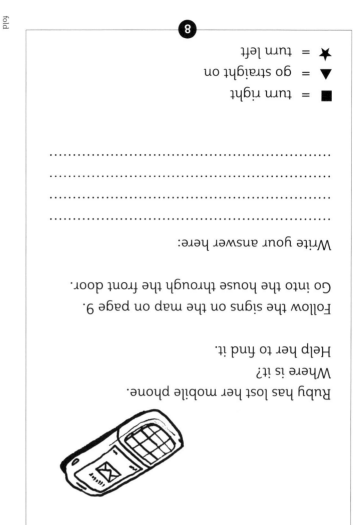

C

D

E

In my house these things are in these rooms:

The hall	
The kitchen	
The dining room	
The sitting room	
My bedroom	
The bathroom	
My parents' room	
My brother's/sister's room	
The cellar	
The study	
The garden	

Who lives in these homes?

1. 742 Evergreen Terrace, Springfield

2. The Imperial Palace, Tokyo

3. 4 Privet Drive, Little Whinging, Surrey

4. Buckingham Palace, London, England

5. 221B Baker Street, London

6. The White House, Washington

7. The Kremlin, Moscow

Here is a list of things you find in a house.
Put A, B, C, etc, in each room where these
things are in your house.

Table A

Television B

Bookcase C

Computer E

Radio F

Curtains D

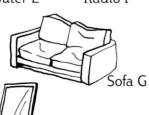
Sofa G

Armchair H

Mirror I

Plant J

a. The Emperor of Japan

b. The Queen of England

c. Harry Potter

d. The President of Russia

e. Bart Simpson

f. The President of the USA

g. Sherlock Holmes

ANSWERS

Pages 2 & 3

1 chef, 2 mechanic, 3 dentist, 4 journalist, 5 fireman, 6 teacher, 7 policeman, 8 bus driver

Pages 4 & 5

saucepan – chef, gun – soldier, tractor – farmer, spanner – mechanic, camera – photographer, thermometer – nurse, computer – journalist, pair of scissors – hairdresser, ladder – fireman, book – teacher

Pages 6 & 7

Indoor jobs: doctor, lawyer, teacher, chef, computer programmer

Outdoor jobs: policeman, postman, soldier, farmer, footballer, fireman, builder

Pages 8 & 9

1 doctor: physics, maths, biology, chemistry
2 architect: maths, art, design and technology, computer studies
3 interpreter: English, French
4 bank manager: maths, English, computer studies
5 chef: cookery
6 photographer: art, design and technology, computer studies
7 journalist: English, history, geography, computer studies

Pages 10 & 11

Sinita is a		**m**	echanic
Nelly is a	ph	**o**	tographer
Jack is a		**d**	entist
Elena is a	ch	**e**	f
Ethan is a	p	**l**	umber

Brad is a **model**.

Pages 12 & 13

1 brave, 2 practical, 3 sporty, 4 intelligent, 5 artistic, 6 money, 7 languages, 8 people, 9 animals, 10 children

EXPLOITATION IDEAS

What am I?

Using the same principle as the Who am I? game in the 'My Home' minibook, assign 13 of the 14 jobs mentioned on pages 2 & 3 of the 'Jobs' minibook to the 13 students in the class and assign one job to yourself. They have to guess each others' jobs just by asking:

…, *are you a fireman? etc.*

They are only allowed one question and if they are correct, the person they have asked drops out of the game (i.e. if he/she is a fireman). They are not allowed to ask you any questions. If they are wrong, the person they have asked now gets to ask someone else a question. As with the other game, the skill is in remembering all the names of the jobs. The game finishes when everyone has been identified, even you. This is good practice in pronunciation of all the job names.

Tools for the job

After your students have completed pages 4 and 5 of the minibook, see if they can remember the objects and the jobs by doing these mini interviews around the class. Begin by saying to Student A: *Does a dentist use a spanner?*

Student A either answers *Yes, he does* and the class decides if she is right or wrong, or: *No, a mechanic uses a spanner.*

She then turns to the next student and asks another question, e.g. *Does a fireman use a tractor?*

Indoors or outdoors

See if your students (in their own language) can think up some more jobs which are done indoors or outdoors. Take a vote to find out how many people would like to work outdoors and how many would like to work indoors.

From school to work

Write a few more jobs on the blackboard and ask the students which subjects they think they would need to study if they wanted to follow that career path.

Card game

If you have an old pack of cards which you are happy to lose, you can create a game of 'Happy Families'. Split the pack into groups of four. Each group represents a family where one member (either the husband or wife) has one of the jobs mentioned in the minibook. You will also have to create family names for each of the jobs, e.g. *Mr Field, the farmer, Mrs Gun, the soldier*. Stick the family names over the real markings on the groups of cards, e.g. *Mr Field, the farmer, Mrs Field, the farmer's wife, Master Field, the farmer's son, Miss Field, the farmer's daughter*.

Shuffle the pack and let four of the students play. (If you are happy to make several of these packs then more students can play.)

Students are dealt eight cards each and the aim is to make two complete families. Student A asks the student on his/her left:

Have you got Miss Gun, the soldier's daughter? if he/she has decided to collect the Gun family. If that student who has been asked has that card, they must hand it to Student A. Student A discards a card from his/her hand onto a central pile if they manage to acquire Miss Gun. The game finishes when the first student with two complete families puts them down on the table.

What are you afraid of?

Write these words on the board, demonstrate how to say them and get your class to repeat the words after you. See if your students know any of these fears and phobias in their mother tongue:

blood, flying, dogs, guns, heights, bees, being alone, feathers, cats, crowds, darkness, dentists, dirt, dogs, fire, ghosts, horses, injections, insects, mice, monsters, number 13, open spaces, snakes, spiders, strangers, trees, thunderstorms, water (the sea).

There are people all over the world who experience these fears. Does anyone in the class share any of these fears or know anyone who does? How would they help someone and what advice would they give to a person who admitted to one of these fears?

Careers advice/pair work

This next exercise requires confidence in English as well as confidence in talking about oneself. Some students might be too shy to reveal too much about themselves or may simply have no idea about what they want to do when they are older. If this is the case, omit this exercise as it will be embarrassing for some of them and you don't want them to feel uncomfortable in the English class.

Ask your students to work in pairs. Once your students have completed pages 14–16 which are their own personal profiles, they can read out the profile based on their answers to their partner, e.g. *I'm practical and brave. I want to work outdoors. At school my best subjects are science, geography and sport. I'm afraid of nothing and I'm good with my hands. When I'm older I want to be a farmer. For this I need to be able to drive a tractor.*

The partner can then offer some extra advice based on the sentence structures already provided in these pages, e.g., *You need to…. You must be good at/good with… You need to be … You need to learn ….*

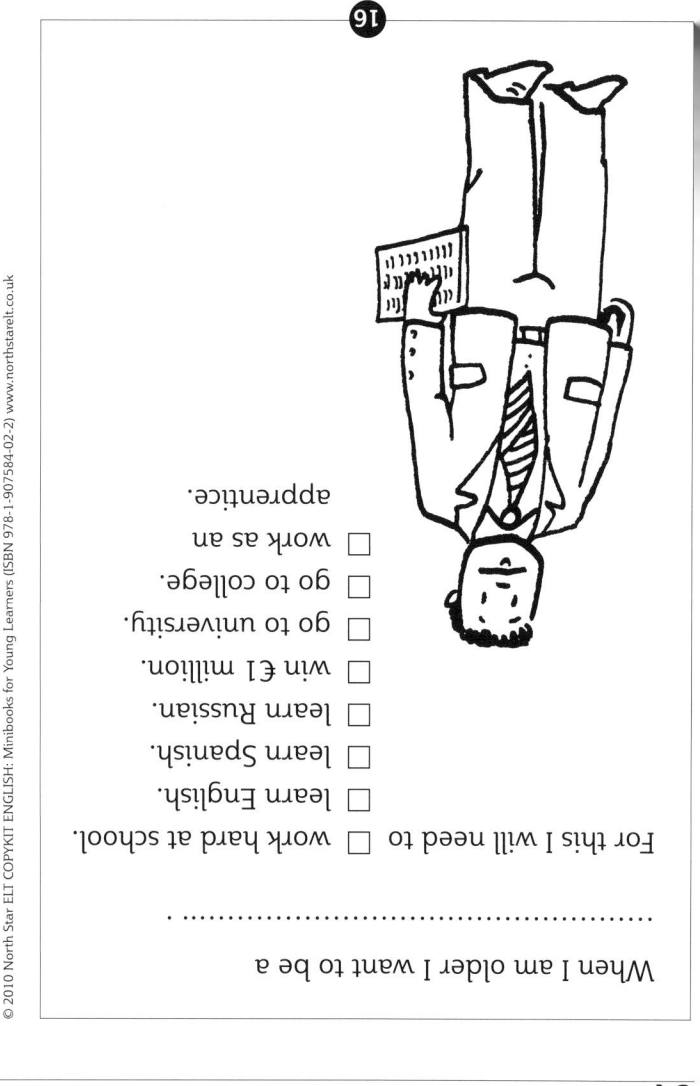

When I am older I want to be a

....

For this I will need to
- [ ] work hard at school.
- [ ] learn English.
- [ ] learn Spanish.
- [ ] learn Russian.
- [ ] win £1 million.
- [ ] go to university.
- [ ] go to college.
- [ ] work as an apprentice.

© 2010 North Star ELT COPYKIT ENGLISH: Minibooks for Young Learners (ISBN 978-1-907584-02-2) www.northstarelt.co.uk

This is a minibook about
Jobs

by ....

---

1. Who uses a saucepan?
- [ ] a farmer
- [ ] a chef

2. Who uses a gun?
- [ ] a vet
- [ ] a soldier

3. Who uses a tractor?
- [ ] a farmer
- [ ] a fireman

4. Who uses a spanner?
- [ ] a dentist
- [ ] a mechanic

5. Who uses a camera?
- [ ] a photographer
- [ ] a nurse

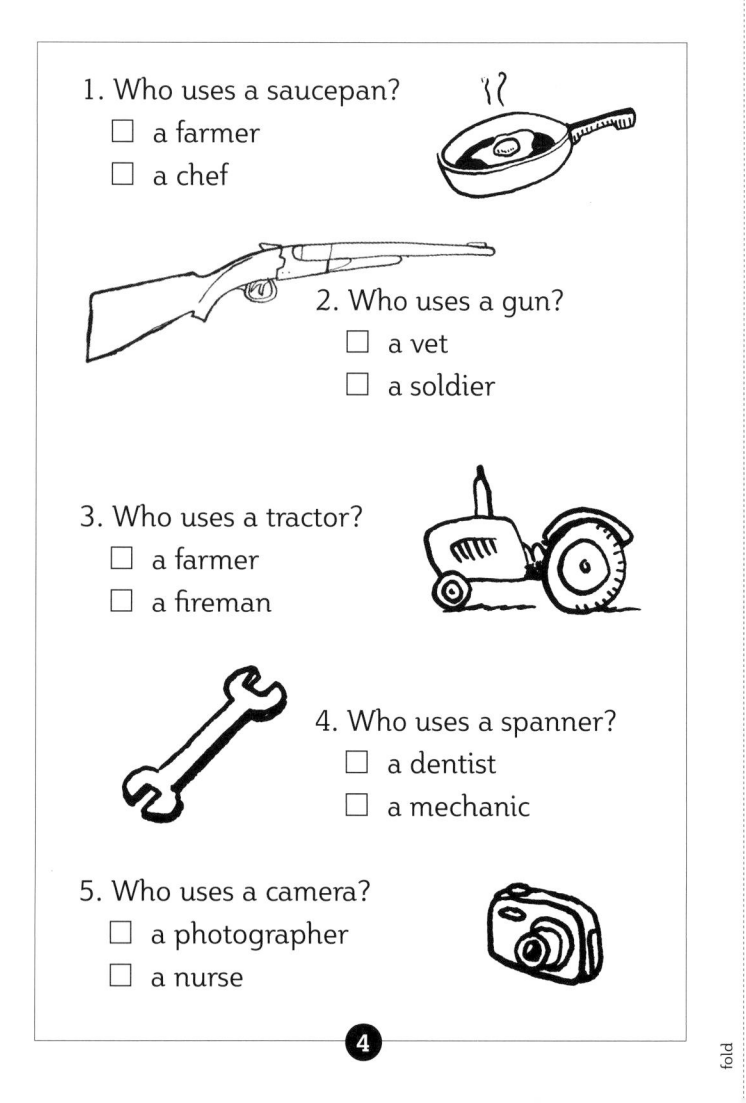

fold

---

6. A bank manager is good with
- [ ] money.
- [ ] words.

7. An interpreter is good with
- [ ] animals.
- [ ] languages.

8. A nurse is good with
- [ ] people.
- [ ] money.

9. A vet is good with
- [ ] animals.
- [ ] words.

10. A teacher is good with
- [ ] guns.
- [ ] children.

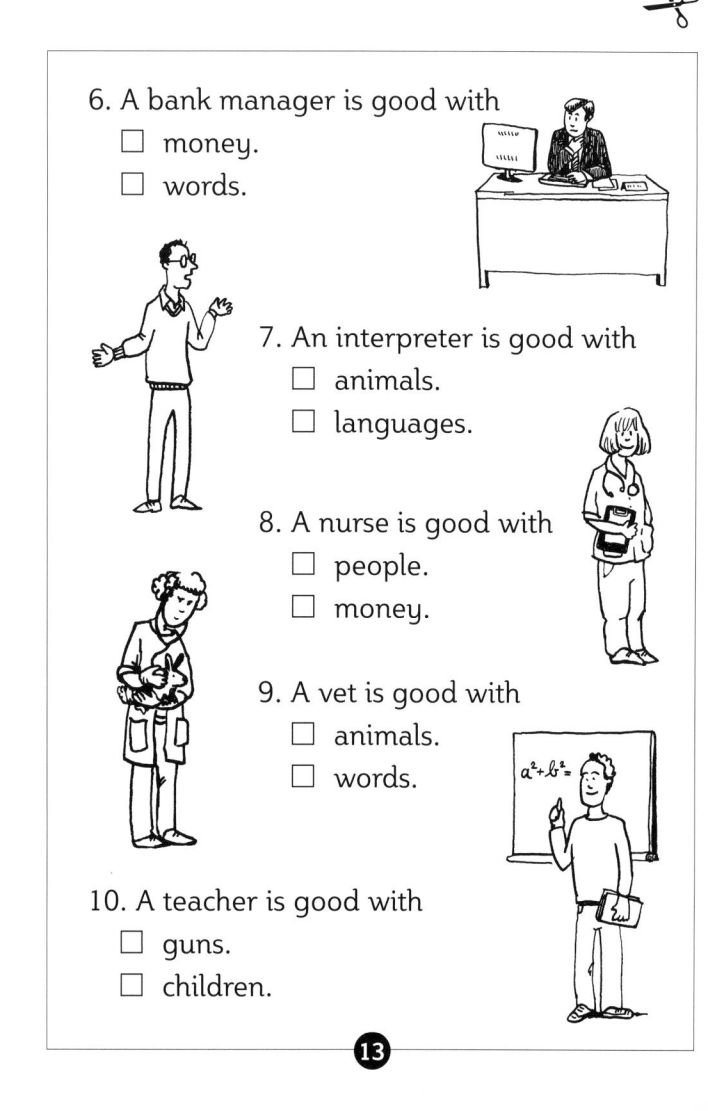

8. She's □ a bus driver □ a hairdresser

7. He's □ a policeman □ a farmer

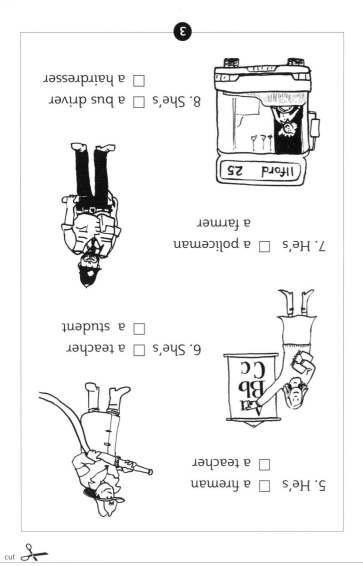

6. She's □ a teacher □ a student

5. He's □ a fireman □ a teacher

cut ✂

---

science, maths, languages, literature,
history, geography, computer studies,
religion, cookery, art, music, sport,
design and technology

....

....

....

....

At school my best subjects are

I want to work □ indoors. □ outdoors.

□ intelligent
□ brave
□ funny
□ sporty
□ musical
□ practical
I am □ artistic

Who are they?

1. He's □ a chef
       □ a grandfather

2. She's □ a mechanic
        □ an actress

3. He's □ a dentist
       □ a postman

4. She's □ a rock star
        □ a journalist

I'm afraid of □ dogs
              □ guns
              □ heights
              □ flying
              □ nothing
              □ ....

I'm good with □ money
              □ languages
              □ children
              □ people
              □ words
              □ my hands
              □ animals

6

A journalist ....

A photographer ....

A chef ....

A bank manager ....

An interpreter ....

An architect ....

A doctor ....

8

What do you need?

Which subjects do you need to study in school to do these jobs?
Write the subjects next to the jobs.

physics
maths
biology
chemistry
English
French
history
geography
music
art
design and technology
sport
cookery
computer studies
religion

12

1. A soldier needs to be
   ☐ brave.
   ☐ funny.

2. A mechanic needs to be
   ☐ artistic.
   ☐ practical.

3. A footballer needs to be
   ☐ sporty.
   ☐ funny.

4. A journalist needs to be
   ☐ intelligent.
   ☐ practical.

5. A hairdresser needs to be
   ☐ musical.
   ☐ artistic.

5

6. Who uses a thermometer?
   ☐ a journalist
   ☐ a nurse

7. Who uses a computer?
   ☐ a chef
   ☐ a journalist

8. Who uses a pair of scissors?
   ☐ a fireman
   ☐ a hairdresser

9. Who uses a ladder?
   ☐ a hairdresser
   ☐ a fireman

10. Who uses a book?
    ☐ a teacher
    ☐ a soldier

Outdoors

Indoors

Now write their jobs on page 11.

1. Sinita is afraid of blood so she can't be a
☐ mechanic.
☐ doctor.

2. Nelly is afraid of flying so she can't be a
☐ photographer.
☐ pilot.

3. Jack is afraid of dogs so he can't be a
☐ vet.
☐ dentist.

4. Elena is afraid of guns so she can't be a
☐ chef.
☐ soldier.

5. Ethan is afraid of heights so he can't be a
☐ fireman.
☐ plumber.

Indoors or Outdoors?

Who works indoors and who works outdoors?

Look at the jobs and write them in the boxes on page 7.

footballer

lawyer

doctor

postman

policeman

soldier

farmer

chef

teacher

builder

fireman

computer programmer

Sinita is a   ☐ _ _ _ _ _ _

Nelly is a   _ _ ☐ _ _ _ _ _ _ _ _

Jack is a   ☐ _ _ _ _ _

Elena is a   _ _ ☐ _

Ethan is a   _ ☐ _ _ _ _

What is Brad's job?

Look at the word in the little boxes above.

ANSWERS

Pages 2 & 3

1 water, 2 toothpaste, 3 crisps, 4 orange juice,
5 chocolate, 6 matches, 7 flowers, 8 lemonade,
9 potatoes, 10 sardines

Pages 4 & 5

1 bottle, 2 tube, 3 packet, 4 carton, 5 bar, 6 box,
7 bunch, 8 can, 9 bag, 10 tin

Page 6

She is going to the butcher's and the greengrocer's,
so she is going to buy chicken and peas.

Pages 8 & 9

milk – dairy, beef – meat, cornflakes – breakfast
cereals, lemonade – soft drinks, wine – alcohol,
potatoes – vegetables, washing powder – household,
apples – fruit

Page 10

APP	**L**	E
ORANG	**E**	
U	**M**	BRELLA
C	**O**	W
BA	**N**	ANA
C	**A**	R
	D	OG
CAM	**E**	L

Page 11

2 – How much do I owe you?

Page 13

She passes the chemist's, the jeweller's, the sweet
shop and the greengrocer's, so she buys medicine,
a necklace, a bar of chocolate and some carrots.

Page 14

You can't buy a new telephone or a newspaper.

Page 16

The florist sells flowers; the butcher sells lamb; the
chemist sells medicine; the music shop sells CDs, the
jeweller sells earrings, the travel agent sells holidays;
the greengrocer sells vegetables; the sweet shop sells
chocolate; the fishmonger sells fish and the post office
sells stamps. The answers spell (vertically) the word
NEWSAGENT'S, so you can buy **newspapers** there.

EXPLOITATION IDEAS

Vocabulary

In the first four pages of the minibook a lot of new
vocabulary is introduced. It will help a great deal if
you bring an example of each of the following into
class:

a bunch of something (flowers, parsley, etc), a bottle
of water, a tube of toothpaste, a tin (of fish, dog food,
etc), a can of lemonade, a bar of soap or chocolate,
a packet (of nuts, crisps), a bag (of flour, potatoes), a
carton of milk. You can also bring in *a pot* of yoghurt,
a box of breakfast cereal, and *a jar* of jam (although
pot, box and jar don't feature on pages 4 and 5).
Hold up each container in turn and ask:
What can you buy in a bottle/can/bar? etc.
If you get your students to bring in one thing
each from home, you can create a little shop in
the classroom and display all the goods. One by
one students can go to the 'shop' and practise the
following dialogue:

Student: *Excuse me, I'd like a …… (tube of
               toothpaste, can of lemonade, etc)*
Shopkeeper: *Yes, of course, here you are. That's one
               pound / sixty pence / ninety
               pence, etc.*
Student: *Thank you very much.*
Shopkeeper: *Would you like anything else?*
Student: *No, that's all, thank you. Goodbye.*

Try to let each student in the class take a turn at
buying something or being the shopkeeper so that
these new words all become completely familiar
before you move on to the different types of shops.

Role play

Type out the list of the shops featured on page 7 of the minibook and make about ten photocopies. Cut these into strips so that each of the shop names is separate. Appoint eleven 'shopkeepers' and then give out the following shopping lists to the remaining students in the class.

List 1: *a mackerel, a necklace, a Girls Aloud CD, headache tablets, a bunch of roses*

List 2: *a chicken, a bar of chocolate, a Harry Potter novel, a pair of jeans*

List 3: *a piece of beef, a bunch of lilies, a sweater, a ring*

List 4: *a teddy bear, a kilo of potatoes, a kilo of carrots, toothpaste*

List 5: *an Agatha Christie novel, two herrings, some chewing gum, a bunch of daffodils*

List 6: *a salmon, a shirt, a leg of lamb, a Barbie doll, a cabbage*

You will need to photocopy the lists for the number of students you have who will be customers. Immediately after you have given them the lists, tell them to go 'shopping'. Each shop they choose to visit will give them a slip with the name of that shop (e.g. *the chemist's*). They collect each of the slips until they think they have done their shopping. NB: They don't actually have to buy anything or do any kind of transaction. The first person to come back to you with all the correct slips of paper corresponding to the items on their shopping list is the winner.

Giving directions

Use the same names for the shops as in the previous exercise. This time, write the shop names much larger and put them in front of random students in the class. One student is then chosen to stand by the classroom door and picks the name of a shop out of a box/hat, etc. He then says to one of the other students who is not a 'shopkeeper' *Excuse me, can you tell me the way to the chemist's / bookshop / butcher's?* etc. That student then has to give instructions through the desks to the correct 'shop' (*Turn left, turn right, go straight on, etc*).

Page 8

Where can you find these things in the supermarket?

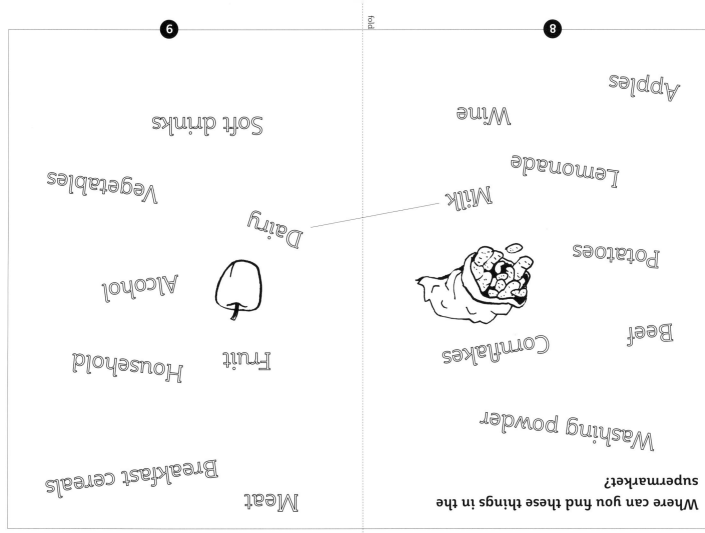

Wine

Apples

Lemonade

Milk —— Dairy

Potatoes

Cornflakes

Beef

Washing powder

Page 6

Soft drinks

Vegetables

Alcohol

Fruit

Household

Breakfast cereals

Meat

© 2010 North Star ELT COPYKIT ENGLISH: Minibooks for Young Learners (ISBN 978-1-907584-02-2) www.northstarelt.co.uk

Find the name of another shop in the town. Write the letter after the correct answer in the space.

The florist sells	N	medicine [W]
The butcher sells	__	CDs [S]
The chemist sells	__	holidays [G]
The music shop sells	__	chocolate [N]
The jeweller sells	__	lamb [E]
The travel agent sells	__	flowers [N]
The greengrocer sells	__	earrings [A]
The sweet shop sells	__	vegetables [E]
The fishmonger sells	__	stamps [S]
The post office sells	__	herring [T]

What can you buy there?

☐ clothes
☐ sausages
☐ stamps
☐ newspapers

This is a minibook about

Shopping

by ....

My three favourite shops are:

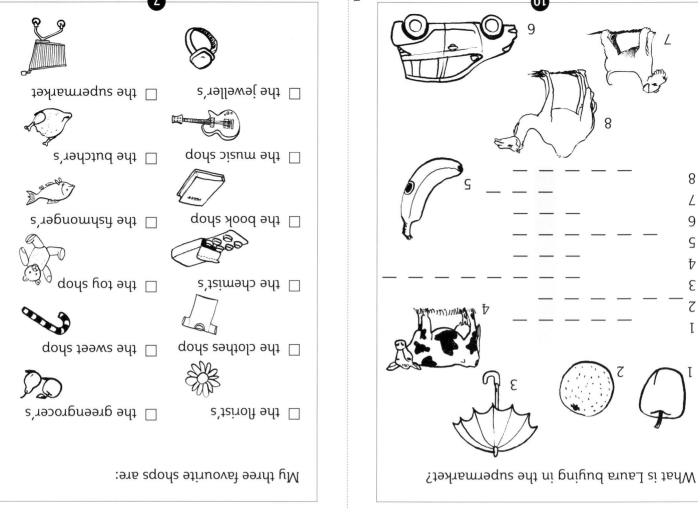

- [ ] the jeweller's
- [ ] the supermarket
- [ ] the music shop
- [ ] the butcher's
- [ ] the book shop
- [ ] the fishmonger's
- [ ] the chemist's
- [ ] the toy shop
- [ ] the clothes shop
- [ ] the sweet shop
- [ ] the florist's
- [ ] the greengrocer's

What is Laura buying in the supermarket?

1
2
3
4
5
6
7
8

Fill in the missing letters.

1. W _ T E _

2. _ _ O _ _ P A S _ E

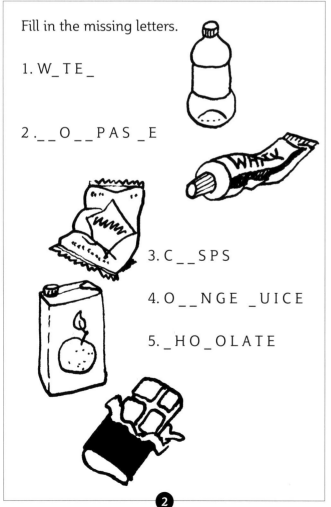

3. C _ _ S P S

4. O _ _ N G E _ U I C E

5. _ H O _ O L A T E

This is my design for a new stamp.

Phoebe is going shopping. Find the shops she visits. What is she going to buy?

She is going to the .... and the ....

flowers   wine   chocolate   fish   chicken   a CD   peas   medicine

---

6. M A _ _ C H E S

7. F _ _ W E R S

8. _ _ M _ N A _ E

9. _ O T _ T O E _

10. S A _ D I N _ S

What does she say at the checkout?

1. I haven't got the money.

2. How much do I owe you?

3. Have you got any money?

Which of these can't you do in a post office?
- buy a stamp
- send a parcel
- post a letter
- buy a new telephone
- buy a postcard
- pay a bill
- buy American dollars
- buy a newspaper

fold

10. .... □ in a packet. □ in a tin.

9. .... □ in a bag. □ in a tube.

8. .... □ in a box. □ in a can.

7. .... □ in a bunch. □ in a bottle.

6. .... □ in a tube. □ in a box.

What is Molly going to buy? Follow her. When she passes a shop, choose a thing from this list:

a necklace	a bar of chocolate
a toy	carrots
a chicken	a book
a CD	flowers
medicine	fish

Key to the shops:
1. the florist's
2. the chemist's
3. the music shop
4. the book shop
5. the travel agent's
6. the jeweller's
7. the sweet shop
8. the butcher's
9. the toy shop
10. the greengrocer's

Write the names of all the foods on pages 2 and 3 in the spaces and tick the correct box.

You can buy

1. .... □ in a bottle.
                   □ in a bag.

2. .... □ in a tube.
                   □ in a tin.

3. .... □ in a packet.
                   □ in a bottle.

4. .... □ in a carton.
                   □ in a bar.

5. .... □ in a bottle.
                   □ in a bar.

She turns first right and then she turns left. She goes straight ahead and takes the second left.

Then she takes the second left again.

She takes the first left and the first right and walks straight home.

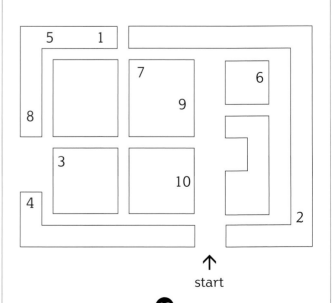

start

ANSWERS

There are no answers as all the activities in this minibook involve describing one's own town.

Page 3
Make sure that your students know that they are required to give a population number to the sentence: ………… *people live in my town.*

EXPLOITATION IDEAS

Project work
As well as doing this project on their own town via a minibook, the class could also work on this as a larger project to present to parents and visitors to the school. It gives all the necessary sentence structures for the students to write quite a long descriptive piece about their town. Whereas individual students will have chosen their own famous buildings for pages 8 & 9 of the minibook, there may be quite a selection of places when everyone's ideas are pooled together. If you are doing it as a class project, students can bring in photos or produce drawings of the places, which can be stuck into a large book or onto large wall posters. Everyone's contributions about favourite shops and restaurants can be pooled together too, and all their collective comments will paint a full picture of their town.

Geography
This minibook involves the students in quite a lot of geography. Make sure they understand the meanings of *north, south, east* and *west.* Also try to ensure that they all have access to an atlas and maps to help them decide on towns which are surrounding the one they have chosen for their minibook, and also to locate the source of rivers and the places where they flow out to the sea.

If your students are unsure about what to write, encourage them to ask you or their fellow students questions in English rather than in the mother tongue, e.g.
Please can you help me? Where does the River … flow to?
What's the name of the theatre in the centre of …?

Festivals and celebrations
When it comes to filling in the information on pages 10 and 11, make sure that your students understand all the different words denoting ways of celebrating in your country. First of all, get the class to brainstorm any other things that they can add to the end of each list and put this selection on the board, and give them the English for these words if they only know them in the mother tongue. Next, brainstorm all the holidays and festivals that are celebrated and get the class to list all the things that happen on those days. This will help everyone choose their own favourite festival to add at the end of page 11.

Antiques Roadshow
This is the name of one of many TV programmes where ordinary members of the public take along objects which they think may be of some value (because of what they are made of, who made them, or their age) to a team of experts. The experts tell them a bit more information about them and also put a value on them so that the owners know what they could make if they sold these items.

Ask your students to bring in anything that is a bit old, but obviously not valuable or breakable! You can then have a 'team of experts' who examine the item, ask the owner a few questions about how his/her family acquired it, whether or not they want to sell it, and then suggest a price. This should all be done in the spirit of a joke, not a serious exercise. The more humorous they can be (in English!), the better.

Tour guide
Ask one of your students to imagine that he/she is a tour guide and has to give a small talk to a group of foreign tourists (played by other students). They can walk around the classroom pointing at imaginary statues, churches, museums, famous buildings, etc. The other 'tourists' can ask questions about them. The 'tour guide' should have prepared some sentences about aspects of the town (all the text is provided by the minibook) while the 'tourists' should prepare some questions in English:
How big is the town?
How old is it?
Where do the trains go to from this station?

Where can you fly to from this airport?
What's the name of the church? Is it old? Has it got any
tombs inside? (the church)
How many students go there? / How do most of them
get to school/university? (the school/university)
What kind of things can you see in the museum?
Is there a river in the town? Where does it flow to?

There's a hospital in my town called
....
☐ and I was born there.
☐ but I wasn't born there.

I went there
☐ to visit ....
☐ when I was ill.
☐ when I broke my arm/leg.
☐ when I had an operation.

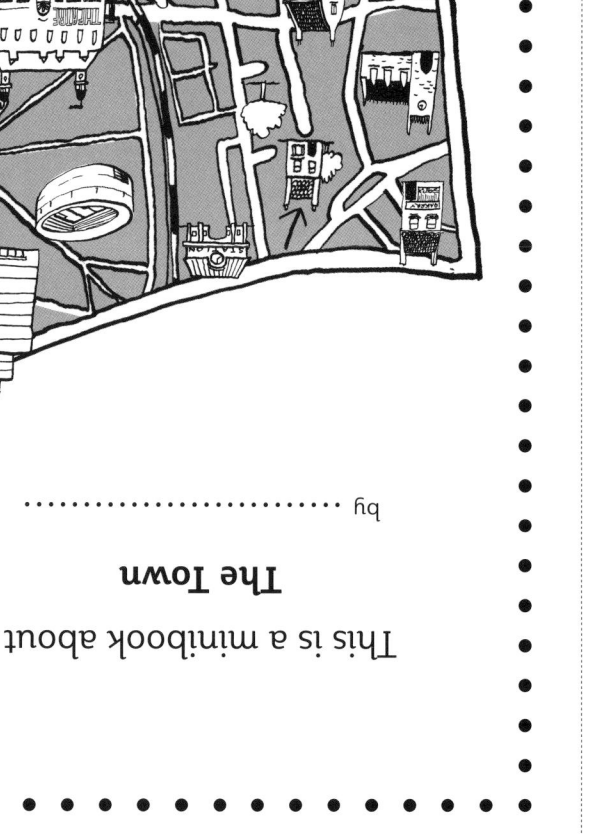

This is a minibook about
The Town

by ....

In July and August people
☐ come to my town for their holidays.
☐ leave my town for their holidays.

There's an important building in my town called
....

There's a statue in my town of
....

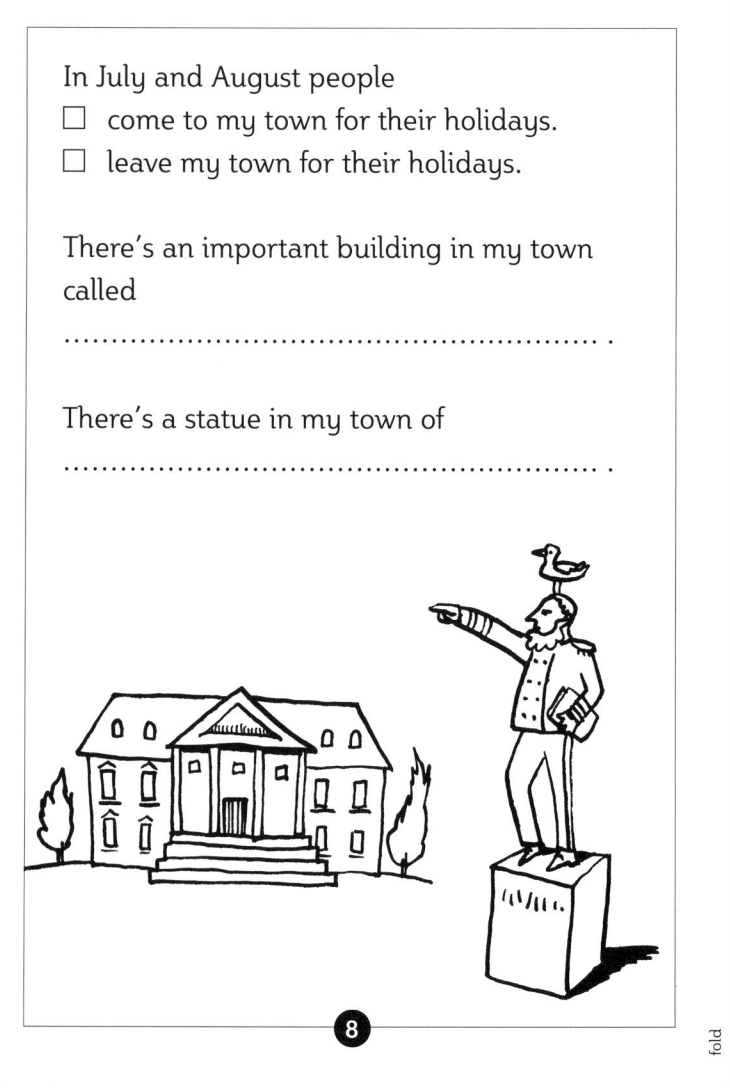

fold

There's a theatre in my town called
....

☐ My town hasn't got a theatre.

The nearest river is the ....

It starts in .... and
flows to ....

7

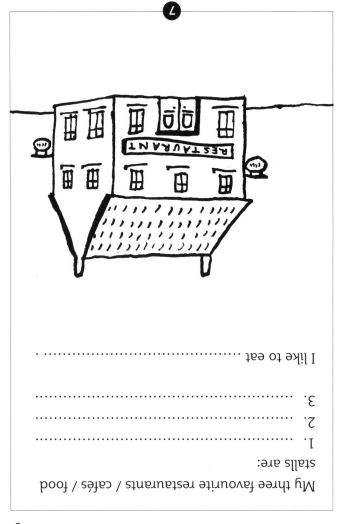

My three favourite restaurants / cafés / food stalls are:

1. ....
2. ....
3. ....

I like to eat ....

10

My town doesn't celebrate Christmas. ☐

My town celebrates Christmas with
☐ fireworks
☐ a big tree
☐ music
☐ people in special costumes
☐ coloured lights
☐ a bonfire
☐ bells
☐ parties
☐ a parade

and ....

cut ✂

2

☐ I live in a town.
☐ I live near a town.
☐ I live a long way from a town.

It's called ....
and it's in ....
(*country*)

☐ It's a small town.
☐ It's a medium-sized town.
☐ It's a big town.
☐ It's the capital city.

Most of the people in this town speak
.... (*French, Italian, etc*)

15

There are .... schools in this town
☐ and also a university.
☐ but no university.

My own school is called ....
and it's .... years old.

There are .... students in the school.

Most of them ☐ live near the school.
 ☐ live in the school.
 ☐ go to school by bus.
 ☐ go to school by car.
 ☐ cycle to school.
 ☐ go to school by train.

☐ My town doesn't celebrate New Year.

My town celebrates New Year with
- ☐ fireworks
- ☐ a big tree
- ☐ music
- ☐ people in special costumes
- ☐ coloured lights
- ☐ a bonfire
- ☐ bells
- ☐ parties
- ☐ a parade

and ....

My town also celebrates ....
(*Easter, Mardi Gras, etc*)
with

....
....
....

The supermarket we use is called
....
It's ☐ in the centre of town.
☐ on the outskirts of the town.

My three favourite shops in the town are:
1. ....
2. ....
and ....

The biggest bookshop in the town is called
....

The last book I bought was
....

☐ The town doesn't have a bookshop.

There's a ☐ church in this town.
☐ cathedral

It's called

....

- ☐ It's a modern building,
- ☐ It's more than 50 years old,
- ☐ It's more than 100 years old,
- ☐ It's more than 300 years old,

- ☐ but it hasn't got any tombs inside.
- ☐ and it's got some ancient tombs.

You ☐ can
☐ can't

climb up to ☐ the tower of the church.
☐ the roof.

My town is north of ....
(*a big town, river or region*)
It's south of ....
It's east of ....
It's west of ....

.... people live in my town.
- ☐ It's a new town.
- ☐ It's an old town.

Here is a photo of my town.

In my town
- [ ] there's one museum.
- [ ] there are lots of museums.
- [ ] there are no museums.

My favourite museum is called
....

You can find these things in it:
- [ ] paintings
- [ ] costumes
- [ ] stamps
- [ ] photographs

The name of the railway station is
....
From my station you can get a direct train to
.... , ... or
....

- [ ] There isn't a railway station in my town.
- [ ] There's also an airport.
- [ ] The town hasn't got an airport.

Here are three facts about my town:

1. ....
....
2. ....
....
3. ....
....

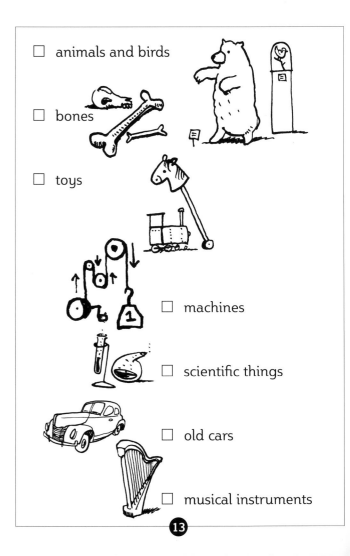

- [ ] animals and birds
- [ ] bones
- [ ] toys
- [ ] machines
- [ ] scientific things
- [ ] old cars
- [ ] musical instruments

ANSWERS

Pages 2 & 3
1 dog, 2 canary, 3 cat, 4 rabbit

Page 6

t	o	r	t	o	i	s	e
f	o	a	u	r	g	s	k
u	c	t	i	d	r	n	a
p	a	r	r	o	t	e	n
f	i	s	h	g	a	p	s
i	g	t	i	b	b	a	r
h	a	m	s	t	e	r	s

(tortoise, parrot, fish, rabbit, hamster, snake, dog, rat, cat, horse). Lawrence has four guinea pigs.

Page 7
1 Max, 2 angry

Pages 8 & 9
Dog – puppy, hen – chick, cat – kitten, horse – foal, sheep – lamb, duck – duckling, cow – calf, pig – piglet, frog – tadpole

Page 10
Good for dogs: biscuits (dog biscuits of course!), beef, chicken, lamb
Bad for dogs: chocolate, grapes, onions, coffee, wine

Page 11
If you give lettuce to your rabbit, it will make it ill.

Page 12
Dogs yawn when they are nervous.
The world's oldest dog lived to the age of 29.

Page 13
1 true, 2 false (they sweat through their paws), 3 false (they can smell things 14 times better than we can)

Page 14
1 d. Charlie Brown, 2 a. Tarzan, 3 c. Mickey Mouse, 4 b. Tintin

Page 15
Cat: whiskers, fur, claws, paws
Bird: beak, feathers, wing, claws
Tortoise: shell

Page 16

	H	A T
	E	Y E
	D	R U M
	W	I N D O W
F	**I**	S H
	G	U N

The pet's name is Hedwig. It's an owl, and it belongs to Harry Potter.

EXPLOITATION IDEAS

Talking about your pet
This is a chance for students to talk about their own pet (if they have one) or their friend's pet or their grandparents' pet (if they don't have one). Many children long for a pet but are either unable to have one because of rules and conditions relating to their house, or because their parents don't want the responsibility of owning and looking after a pet.
If some students have pets which are not mentioned in the lists in the first few pages of the minibook, write them up on the board so that everyone becomes familiar with the vocabulary.

Find out who definitely has a pet. Ask:
What kind of pet have you got?
What's its name?
How old is it?
Can you describe ……? (pet's name)
What does it eat?
How much does it cost to keep your pet?
Have you ever taken your pet to the vet?
How often do you feed it? (once a day/twice a day, etc)
Can it do any special tricks?
Who do you all think has the most unusual pet in this class?

Pet game

Get the children to come up to the front of the class one by one and do a mime of something they do whilst looking after an imaginary pet. The class have to guess what kind of pet this could be from the mime. For example, it could be shaking some fish food into a fish tank, grooming a dog or cat, handling a snake, etc. Encourage them to think of more unusual kinds of pets and more amusing actions.

Animal behaviour

Pages 12 and 13 of the minibook: Tell your students that dogs yawn when they are nervous, hamsters are aggressive and fight one another, dogs sweat through their paws, and cats have a good sense of smell.

Ask your students if they know any other important facts about pets that they can share with the class, either those that they have observed with their own pets, or those that they have seen on TV or read about. For homework, you could ask everyone to find one interesting fact about pet behaviour (not wild animals) and come to class and tell everyone about it at the next lesson. The class can decide which is the most interesting and surprising of all the pieces of information that are shared.

Famous pets

On page 14 there is a small quiz about famous pets. Ask your students:
How many famous pets can you name?
Can you remember any famous dogs from films you have seen?
Write the list on the board. Quite a lot of Hollywood movies have featured dogs or cats (e.g. Garfield, Beethoven, Lassie).
Do any stars in your own country have pets? If so, who and what? Is there a pet which appears regularly on TV in your own country?
Ask:
Which is your favourite cinema or TV pet?
Take a class vote once the list has been created.

Sending an 'owl'

Page 16 of the minibook introduces Harry Potter's pet owl, Hedwig. In the Harry Potter books by J K Rowling, 'owls' are messages like telegrams, i.e. faster than regular mail. They are called 'owls' because actual owls deliver them.

Give everyone a piece of paper and get them to compose an 'owl' in English to someone else in the class. They must write the name of the person on the outside of the folded paper. Then one student can volunteer to be Hedwig and can deliver all the 'owls' around the class.

foal
kitten
lamb
puppy
chick
calf
tadpole
duckling
piglet

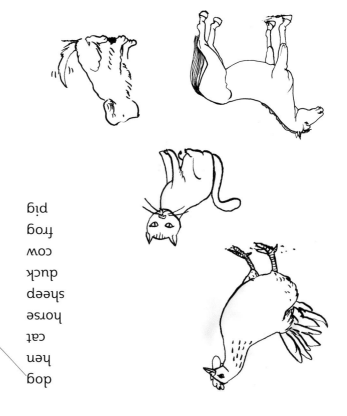

Baby animals are really cute. Match the animal to the baby.

dog
hen
cat
horse
sheep
duck
cow
frog
pig

© 2010 North Star ELT COPYKIT ENGLISH: Minibooks for Young Learners (ISBN 978-1-907584-02-2) www.northstarelt.co.uk

This pet belongs to a famous character from books and films. What is it? What's its name? Whose pet is it?

1 _ _ _
2 _ _ _ _
3 _ _ _ _
4 _ _ _ _ _ _
5 _ _ _ _
6 _ _ _

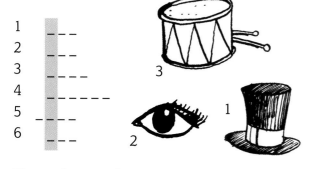

The pet's name is ....
It's an .... ,
and it belongs to ....

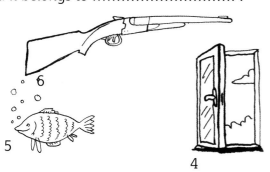

This is a minibook about

Pets

by ....

Page 7

The most popular name for a pet dog in America is

- ☐ Barack.
- ☐ Max.
- ☐ George.

When a dog is happy, it wags its tail quickly.

When a cat is

- ☐ happy
- ☐ tired
- ☐ angry

it wags its tail quickly.

Page 10

DOG

It's good to give your dog…
(Choose from the list below)

....
....

It's bad to give your dog…
(Choose from the list below)

....
....

chocolate	biscuits	grapes
onions	beef	coffee
chicken	wine	lamb

Page 2

1. It wags its tail when it's happy.
   - ☐ tortoise
   - ☐ parrot
   - ☐ fish
   - ☐ dog

2. It can sing well.
   - ☐ dog
   - ☐ canary
   - ☐ tortoise
   - ☐ rabbit

Page 15

Write the words *cat, tortoise* or *bird* next to these body parts. Sometimes the things in the list belong to more than one of them.

beak

whiskers

feathers

fur

wing

claws

shell

paws

cut

Page 11

If you give
- ☐ carrots
- ☐ lettuce
- ☐ apples
- ☐ cabbage

to your rabbit, it will get sick.

Page 9

Find the ten pets and colour all the other squares yellow.

What pets does Lawrence have?

You can read the answer in the yellow squares.

Put the letters here: ____ _____ ____

t	o	r	t	o	i	s	e
f	o	a	u	r	g	s	k
u	c	t	i	d	n	a	a
p	a	r	r	o	t	e	n
f	i	s	h	g	e	p	s
i	g	t	i	b	b	a	r
h	a	m	s	t	e	r	s

Page 14

Famous pets quiz

1. Who owned a dog called Snoopy?

   ....

2. Who owned a chimpanzee called Cheeta?

   ....

3. Who owned a dog called Pluto?

   ....

4. Who owned a dog called Snowy?

   ....

a. Tarzan
b. Tintin
c. Mickey Mouse
d. Charlie Brown

Page 3

3. It likes to kill mice.
   - ☐ rabbit
   - ☐ frog
   - ☐ cat
   - ☐ canary

4. It has long ears and soft fur.
   - ☐ parrot
   - ☐ cat
   - ☐ rabbit
   - ☐ snake

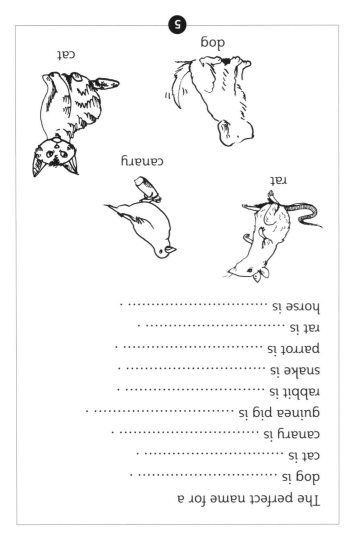

cat

dog

canary

rat

The perfect name for a

dog is ....

cat is ....

canary is ....

guinea pig is ....

rabbit is ....

snake is ....

parrot is ....

rat is ....

horse is ....

People yawn when they are tired.

Dogs yawn when they are ☐ tired.

☐ happy.

☐ nervous.

☐ angry.

The world's oldest dog lived to the age of

☐ 18.

☐ 29.

☐ 61.

I've got a ....

My friend's got a ....

My grandparents have got a

.... called

.... which eats

....

I would love to own a ....

guinea pig

parrot

horse

rabbit

snake

True/False

☐ 1. A hamster doesn't like to live with other hamsters.

☐ 2. When dogs are hot they sweat through their tongues.

☐ 3. Cats can smell things five times better than people.

ANSWERS

Page 3

1 *Parrot* because the other two are mammals; 2 *Zebra* because the other two are reptiles; 3 *Elephant* because the other two are fish; 4 *Panda* because the other two are birds; 5 *Rat* because the other two are *insects*.

Pages 4 & 5

1 elephant: I've got grey skin and a long trunk.
2 lion: I am king of the animals. I've got brown fur.
3 rhino: I'm fat and I've got two horns on my nose.
4 tarantula: I've got eight hairy legs.
5 panda: I've got black and white fur and I eat bamboo.
6 giraffe: I've got a long neck and yellow fur with brown spots.

Pages 6 & 7

1 penguin: I'm black and white and I love swimming.
2 ostrich: I'm a bird but I can't fly. Each of my eggs weighs 1.5kg.
3 parrot: I can speak like a person. I've got coloured feathers.
4 crocodile: I live for 75 years. I weigh 900kg and I can swim.
5 python: I'm ten metres long and I weigh over 110kg.
6 chameleon: My tongue is longer than my body and I can change the colour of my skin.

Pages 8 & 9

1 camel, 2 gorilla, 3 giraffe, 4 zebra, 5 polar bear, 6 panda, 7 Bengal tiger, 8 kangaroo, 9 koala bear, 10 tarantula, 11 parrot, 12 penguin, 13 bald eagle

Pages 10 & 11

Penguin – fish; kangaroo – grass and leaves; lion – meat; snake – mice; polar bear – seals and fish; ostrich – leaves, seeds, insects, small stones; tarantula – spiders, lizards, snakes, frogs; panda – bamboo

Pages 12 & 13

1 ostrich, 2 rat, 3 Chimpanzees, 4 A kangaroo, 5 The giraffe, 6 Camels

Pages 14 & 15

1 *Madagascar*, 2 *The Jungle Book*, 3 *Dumbo*, 4 *Kung-fu Panda*, 5 *The Lion King*

Page 16

e	l	e	p	h	a	n	t	a	b
t	i	g	e	r	d	c	d	g	s
a	o	r	p	e	n	g	u	i	n
r	n	e	h	f	a	g	o	r	a
a	r	e	d	i	p	s	s	a	k
n	h	i	j	k	n	l	t	f	e
t	f	r	o	g	e	o	r	f	l
u	m	n	o	m	p	q	i	e	r
l	s	t	a	u	v	w	c	x	y
a	z	c	o	p	p	i	h	a	b

(elephant, tiger, penguin, spider, frog, hippo, tarantula, lion, panda, ostrich, giraffe, snake, rhino camel)

EXPLOITATION IDEAS

Find out how many of the students have visited the nearest zoo to your school. What is their favourite thing about it? What's good about zoos and what's bad about zoos?

Animal vocabulary

Before you begin work on the zoo minibook, brainstorm all the names of animals that your class can think of. They will probably know more than they think. Help them out with little clues to elicit a few more, either by giving them the first and last letters, or by giving them clues as to what kind of an animal they are, what size they are, what they eat, etc.

Draw an animal

Take a large piece of paper and give it to one student in the class. Ask him/her just to draw one line on the paper and pass it on to the next student, who must then draw something more and pass it on. The aim is to end up with a recognisable zoo animal, but of course with no one knowing what the initial intention is, the drawing will probably be a little weird!

Animal personality game

This is quite a fun game but you may feel that your students are too sensitive to play it and just treat it as a joke, so it is up to you to use your judgment.

1 *Ask a student: What is your favourite animal?*
Then ask them to give a reason: *I like it because it's* .... (insert an adjective here, e.g. *friendly, funny, cuddly, strong, wild.*)

2 Now ask the same student again:
What is your second favourite animal?
He/she gives a reason: *I like it because it's* ....

3 Now ask the same student again: *What's your third favourite animal?*
He/she gives a reason: *I like it because it's* ....
Now look at the three words from the *I like it because…* answers.

The first word signifies how the student wants to be. The second adjective is how other people see that student. The third adjective is how they really are.

Geography

While your students are thinking about where the animals originate from on the map on pages 8 & 9, use this as a good time to revise the names of countries and nationalities. When you are discussing the various animals, ask your students if they know what they eat. This is good practice for pages 10 & 11. They may be surprised to learn that the ostrich eats stones and that the tarantula has such a large repertoire of foods.

Animal quiz

After your students have completed the quiz on miscellaneous animal facts on pages 12 & 13, ask them to research one more fact that they think will surprise or interest their fellow students (from the Internet or from an encyclopedia). They then have to turn this piece of information into a multiple-choice question in the style of those in the minibook. This way you will be able to have a class animal quiz with as many questions as there are students in your class.

Animals in films

If your students have seen the films mentioned in the film quiz on pages 14 & 15, get them to give you simple sentences about things that happen in the story. If more than five people have seen a film, you should end up with quite a long piece of writing on the board about that film.

How many people cry when they are watching animal films? Explain to them that most adults do, and it's perfectly OK to be sad!

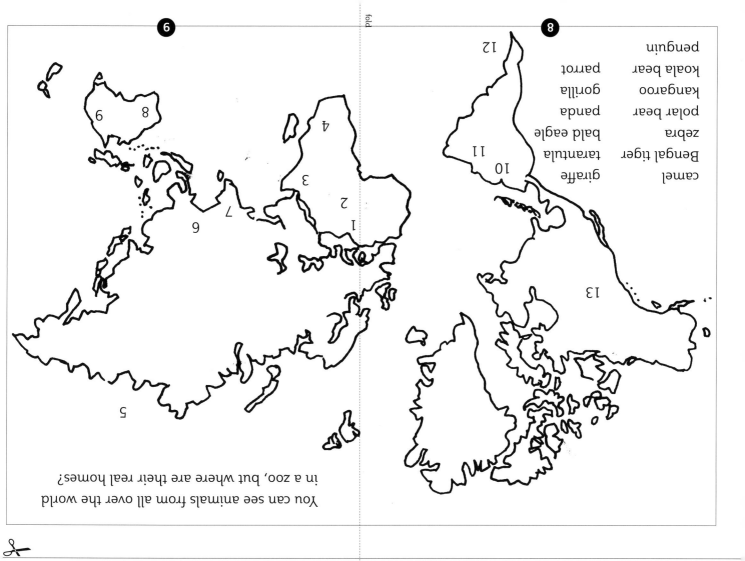

penguin
koala bear parrot
kangaroo gorilla
polar bear panda
zebra bald eagle
Bengal tiger tarantula
camel giraffe

You can see animals from all over the world
in a zoo, but where are their real homes?

Find the 16 animals in the word square.

e	l	e	p	h	a	n	t	a	b
t	i	g	e	r	d	c	d	g	s
a	o	r	p	e	n	g	u	i	n
r	n	e	h	f	a	g	o	r	a
a	r	e	d	i	p	s	s	a	k
n	h	i	j	k	n	l	t	f	e
t	f	r	o	g	e	o	r	f	l
u	m	n	o	m	p	q	i	e	r
l	s	t	a	u	v	w	c	x	y
a	z	c	o	p	p	i	h	a	b

1 ....
2 ....
3 ....
4 ....
5 ....
6 ....
7 ....
8 ....

9 ....
10 ....
11 ....
12 ....
13 ....
14 ....
15 ....
16 ....

© 2010 North Star ELT COPYKIT ENGLISH: Minibooks for Young Learners (ISBN 978-1-907584-02-2) www.northstarelt.co.uk

This is a minibook about

The Zoo

by ....

PLEASE DON'T FEED THE ANIMALS

colour	white	tongue	fly
metres	eggs	crocodile	weigh
python	speak	feathers	ostrich
parrot	penguin	swim	chameleon

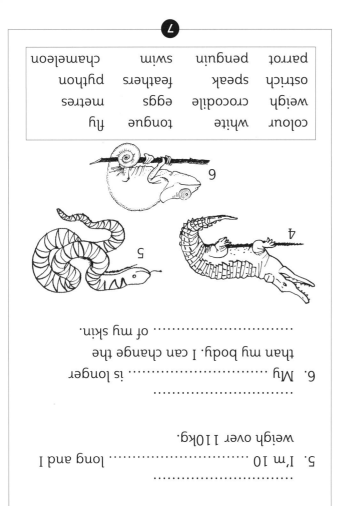

6

5

4

5. I'm 10 .... long and I .... weigh over 110kg.

6. My .... is longer than my body. I can change the .... of my skin.

cut ✂

Match the food to the animal.

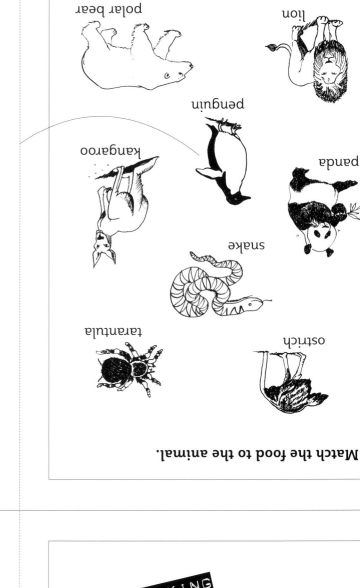

polar bear

lion

penguin

kangaroo

panda

snake

tarantula

ostrich

☐ I like zoos; they are fun.
☐ I don't like zoos; they are cruel.

The nearest zoo to my house is called
....

My first visit to the zoo was when I was
.... years old.

ZOO

TODAY

THE LION KING

KUNG FU PANDA

THE JUNGLE BOOK

MADAGASCAR

DUMBO

CINEMA

TONIGHT

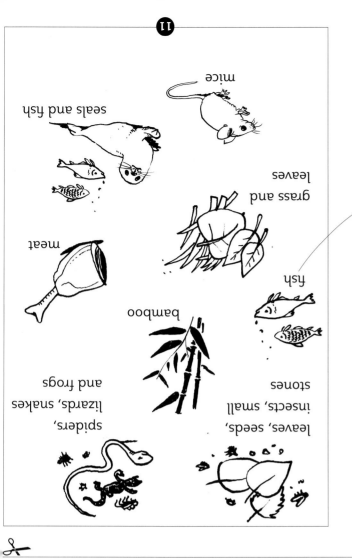

mice

seals and fish

leaves

grass and leaves

meat

fish

bamboo

stones

leaves, seeds, small insects,

spiders, lizards, snakes and frogs

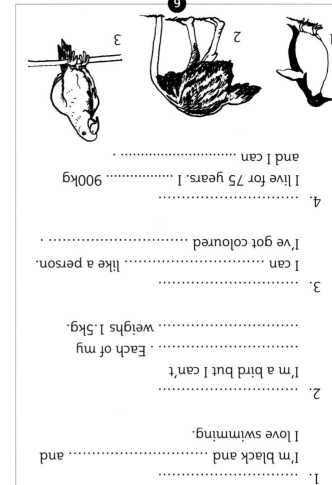

3

2

1

1. I'm black and .... and .... I love swimming.

2. .... I'm a bird but I can't .... Each of my .... weighs 1.5kg.

3. .... I can .... like a person. I've got coloured ....

4. .... I live for 75 years. I .... 900kg and I can ....

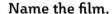

Name the film.

1. A lion, a zebra, a giraffe and a hippo escape from New York Zoo.

2. A panther helps a boy called Mowgli to escape from a cruel tiger.

3. An elephant with very big ears has lots of adventures.

4. A black and white animal learns to do martial arts.

5. A young lion called Simba has a cruel uncle called Scar who wants to be the king, but Simba is finally lucky.

Underline the 'odd one out' in these groups. Fill in the missing words from the box at the bottom of the page.

gorilla lion parrot   because the other two are ....

piranha eel zebra   because the other two are ....

elephant snake lizard   because the other two are ....

panda penguin eagle   because the other two are ....

fly ladybird rat   because the other two are ....

reptiles   fish   mammals   birds   insects

spots	long	panda	legs	neck
giraffe	fat	brown	animals	elephant
nose	eight	lion	yellow	bamboo
fur	grey	rhino	tarantula	

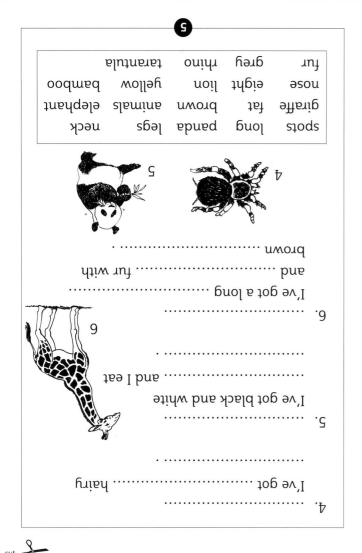

4. I've got ....
.... hairy

5. ....
I've got black and white ....
and I eat ....

6. ....
I've got a long ....
and .... fur with
brown.

1. The
☐ ostrich
☐ elephant
☐ hippopotamus
has got the biggest eyes of all the animals.

2. A baby polar bear is the same size as a
☐ dog
☐ rat
☐ pig
when it is born.

3. ☐ Tigers
☐ Chimpanzees
☐ Pythons
can't swim.

4. ☐ An elephant
☐ A kangaroo
☐ A lion
can't walk backwards.

cut ✂

Write the missing words in the text on pages 4, 5, 6 and 7.

1. ....
I've got .... skin and a
.... trunk.

2. ....
I am the king of the ....
I've got .... fur.

3. ....
I'm .... and I've got
two horns on my ....

1

2

3

5. ☐ The crocodile
☐ The giraffe
☐ The elephant
has got the longest tail of all the animals.

6. ☐ Camels
☐ Lions
live longer than giraffes.

ANSWERS

Pages 6 & 7

1 sandals (They are all night clothes.)
2 T-shirt (They are all trousers.)
3 skirt (They are all kinds of shoes.)
4 sunglasses (They are all things to wear in cold weather.)
She is wearing summer clothes.

Pages 8 & 9

1 The cheapest jeans cost £24.
2 The longest scarf costs £12.
3 There are five hats.
4 The striped jumper is more expensive.

Pages 10 & 11

1 The hat's too big.
2 The jacket's too expensive.
3 The trousers are too short.
4 The shoes look very stupid.

Pages 12 & 13

tro	**u**	sers
ju	**m**	per
	b	oots
sho	**r**	ts
j	**e**	ans
s	**l**	ippers
be	**l**	t
pyj	**a**	mas

Answer = umbrella. You need it when it's raining.

Page 16

s	k	i	r	t	h	a	t	t
h	b	r	j	e	a	n	s	r
o	l	e	a	d	r	e	t	o
e	o	p	c	f	s	s	o	u
s	u	m	k	i	r	n	o	s
u	s	u	e	g	g	a	b	e
i	e	j	t	o	w	n	c	r
t	t	r	a	i	n	e	r	s

(skirt, shoes, suit, hat, blouse, boots, jeans, jumper, trousers, trainers, jacket, scarf)
The other squares spell the word: *dressing-gown*.

EXPLOITATION IDEAS

Describing your own clothes

Before you begin the minibook, get students to make one statement each about their own or someone else's clothes in the class, e.g.
Marco is wearing grey trousers.
Lisa is wearing a pink jumper.
This way you will be pooling the class's knowledge of clothes and colour vocabulary. Provide a word if a student desperately wants to say something but hasn't got the vocabulary. Each new colour and clothes item that you encounter should be written on the board.

Clothes game

Only attempt this game if you have access to quite a lot of large-sized clothes that are more or less unwanted. It needs a lot of organization and is quite energetic, so if you have a class that gets over-excited maybe give this one a miss. However, it's good fun for a Friday or for a day just before the school holidays begin.

Draw out a long 'snake' divided into 36 squares on a sheet of paper. Make it wind back and forth on itself so that it leaves no empty space on the page. Number each of the squares from 1 to 36. Write the following clothes words only in these numbered squares. Leave the others blank:
1 START, 3 SCARF, 5 T-SHIRT, 7 SKI HAT, 8 TRAINERS,

9 JUMPER, 12 TIGHTS, 13 JEANS, 16 BASEBALL CAP, 17 SOCK, 18 SKIRT, 20 SHIRT, 23 GLOVE, 24 BELT, 25 GLOVE, 27 JUMPER, 29 UMBRELLA, 31 BOOT, 32 SOCK, 34 JACKET.

NB You will need each of the above items (two of each if possible) on the floor at the front of the class.

Photocopy the sheet for each person in class.

Choose two students who are the two players while everyone else follows their progress on their sheet.

This pair of players each has a die and a little cup and they sit at the back of the class. When you say 'Go!' they shake their dice and each shout out what number they have. The class mark this on their sheet and then, if this is a blank square, the players shake again. If they land on a square with a clothes word they must race to the front of the class, find the item and put it on and then run back and continue. They may find there is only one example of the item so they will lose a point for this. When they get to the end of the game they get a point for every item they have found correctly and put on, and then a point deducted for items missed. It is then the turn of the next two players, etc. You can add other items to the board game if you are able to bring them into class for the game.

Clothes shop role play
You can use the clothes provided for the game above to create a pretend clothes shop. Maybe tie some price tags on the items and get students to come out and try on one of the items and then make a comment to the assistant who has served them, following the model sentences on page 11 of the minibook. Make sure that the assistant also knows his/her lines, e.g. *Can I help you? What size are you? Try this; I think it will look good. What about this one?*

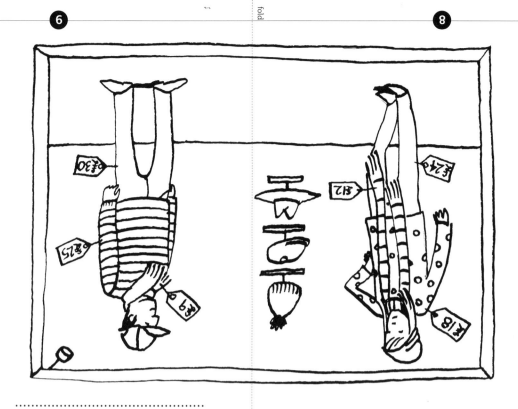

4. Which is more expensive – the spotted jumper or the striped jumper?
....

3. How many hats can you see?
....

fold

2. What does the longest scarf cost?
....

1. What do the cheapest jeans cost?
....

Find these clothes in the grid:

skirt, shoes, suit, hat, blouse, boots, jeans, jumper, trousers, trainers, jacket, scarf

s	k	i	r	t	h	a	t	t
h	b	r	j	e	a	n	s	r
o	l	e	a	d	r	e	t	o
e	o	p	c	f	s	s	o	u
s	u	m	k	i	r	n	o	s
u	s	u	e	g	g	a	b	e
i	e	j	t	o	w	n	c	r
t	t	r	a	i	n	e	r	s
l	s	t	a	u	v	w	c	x
a	z	c	o	p	p	i	h	a

Colour the other squares yellow.
What piece of clothing can you see in the yellow squares? Write it here:

_ _ _ _ _ _ _ _ - _ _ _ _

© 2010 North Star ELT COPYKIT ENGLISH: Minibooks for Young Learners (ISBN 978-1-907584-02-2) www.northstarelt.co.uk

This is a minibook about

Clothes

by ....

She is wearing

☐ summer
☐ winter
clothes.

cut

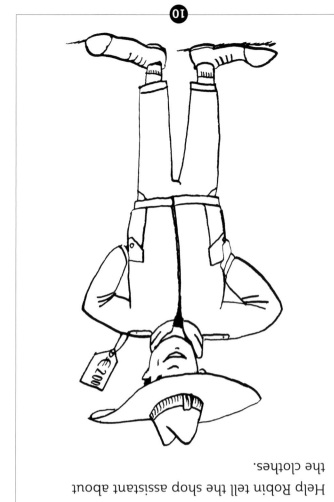

Help Robin tell the shop assistant about
the clothes.

Colour the clothes on page 3.

Ellie is wearing

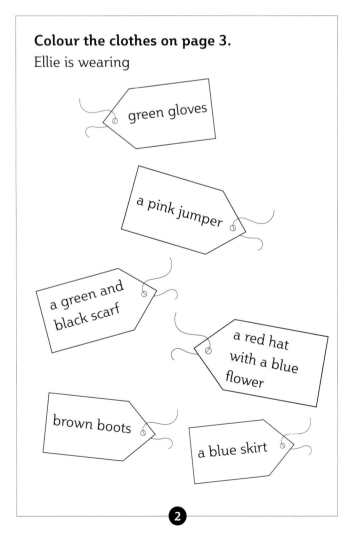

green gloves

a pink jumper

a green and
black scarf

a red hat
with a blue
flower

brown boots

a blue skirt

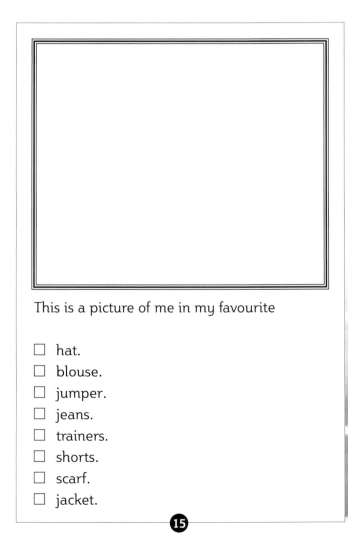

This is a picture of me in my favourite

☐ hat.
☐ blouse.
☐ jumper.
☐ jeans.
☐ trainers.
☐ shorts.
☐ scarf.
☐ jacket.

The shoes look
☐ very smart.
☐ very stupid.

The trousers are
☐ too long
☐ too short.

This jacket's
☐ too cheap.
☐ too expensive.

My hat's
☐ too big
☐ too small.

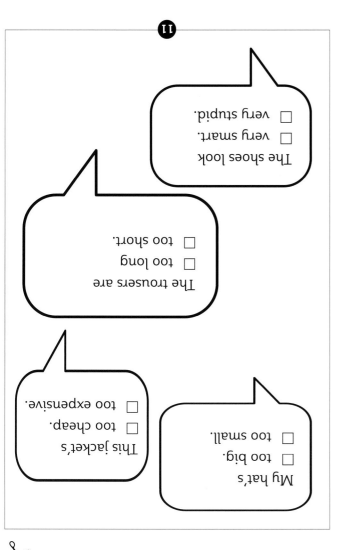

fold

Which is the odd one out in these groups?
Underline the words and then draw them on
Daisy on page 7.

1. pyjamas   3. trainers
dressing gown   skirt
sandals   wellingtons
slippers   shoes

2. T-shirt   4. gloves
trousers   scarf
jeans   coat
shorts   sunglasses

My favourite clothes shop is called

....

The three things I like wearing best of all are:
1. my ....
2. my ....
and
3. my ....

I love
☐ shoes
☐ trainers
☐ jeans
☐ trousers
and I've got .... pairs.

I'd like to borrow my best friend's

....

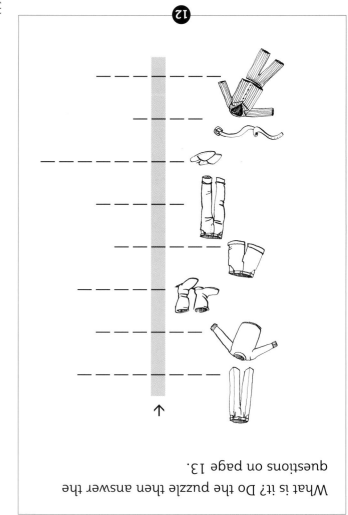

What is it? Do the puzzle then answer the questions on page 13.

cut

fold

Colour the clothes on page 5.

Charlie is wearing

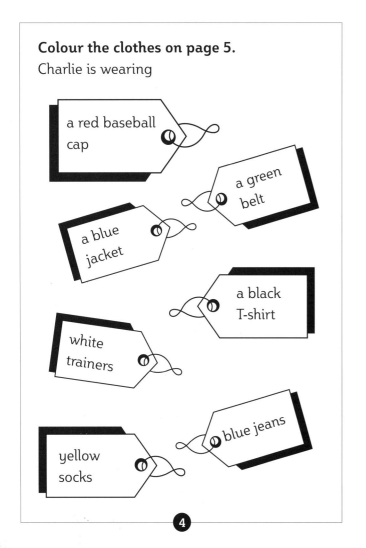

a red baseball cap

a green belt

a blue jacket

a black T-shirt

white trainers

blue jeans

yellow socks

When do you need it?

☐ When it's sunny.
☐ When it's snowing.
☐ When it's raining.

Have you got one of these?
☐ Yes
☐ No
What colour is it? ....

ANSWERS

There are no answers as all the activities in this minibook involve describing one's own preferences in hobbies.

EXPLOITATION IDEAS

Talking about hobbies

This minibook, more than any of the others, is the most personal, since on every page students will be revealing more and more about their own interests and preferences.

Hopefully it covers most of the vocabulary that any of them will need to describe the things they like doing. Inevitably there will be a few omissions, but you can write these words on the board (e.g. scuba diving) to help them.

There is plenty of practice of the *like + -ing* construction here too.

TV interviews role play

Set up a few chairs at the front of the class so that they look like a sofa. Appoint two of the more confident and capable students as the presenters/interviewers of a TV programme called *My Favourite Things*. They can take turns at asking questions if they want, but they should come in the order given below, if possible. Students can take it in turns to come into 'the studio' to be interviewed as if they are celebrities. All the answers they will need to the questions will be in their minibooks once they have completed them. If possible, use a little music to begin the 'programme' and fade it down as the first presenter begins to speak. As the end of the interview finishes, the music can be faded back up. If you have access to a video camera it will be even better.

Here are the interviewer's questions and references to the minibook pages for the relevant answers. However, interviewees should memorize their answers before their 'appearance'. It is important that the 'interviewer' listens carefully to the answers and occasionally makes a little friendly comment if possible.

Fade down music

Presenter: *Hello everyone, and welcome to 'My Favourite Things', everybody's favourite TV programme. On the sofa today we've got Mario, Anna and Jan.*

Mario, we'll start with you first.

What do you like doing in your free time? (pages 2, 3, 4 & 5)

Do you like collecting things? (page 6)

Who's your best friend? Is he/she here in the audience? What does he/she like doing? (page 7)

Do you like sport? (pages 8 & 9)

What's your favourite football team? (page 9)

Who's your favourite tennis player? (page 9)

Can you play a musical instrument? (pages 10 & 11)

What about singing? (page 11)

Who are your favourite male singers? (page 12)

Who are your favourite female singers? (page 12)

Who are your favourite groups? (page 12)

What's your favourite kind of music? (page 13)

What are your favourite TV programmes at the moment? (page 14)

What kind of programmes do you like best? (page 15)

What are your favourite books? (page 16)

What are your favourite films? (page 16)

Presenter: *Well that's all we've got time for today. A big thank you to Mario, Anna and Jan, and make sure you watch tomorrow when our guests will be Jessica, Philip and Andrea. So goodbye from me, until next time…*

Fade up music

6

My favourite football team is
....

My favourite tennis player is
....

8

The sports I like are:

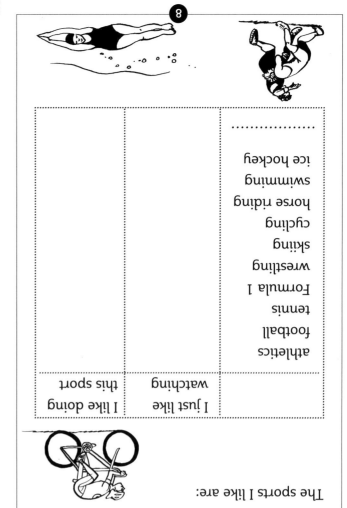

	I just like watching	I like doing this sport
athletics		
football		
tennis		
Formula 1		
wrestling		
skiing		
cycling		
horse riding		
swimming		
ice hockey		
....		

My three favourite books are
1. ....
2. .... and
3. ....

My three favourite films are
1. ....
2. .... and
3. ....

My favourite book is
....

My favourite film is
....

16

This is a minibook about

Hobbies

by ....

I like watching

- [ ] COWBOYS
- [ ] REALITY TV
- [ ] FANTASY
- [ ] HORROR
- [ ] COMEDY
- [ ] QUIZ SHOWS
- [ ] SPORT
- [ ] DRAMA
- [ ] SOAPS

I like going

- [ ] to the cinema.
- [ ] to museums and galleries.
- [ ] to football matches.
- [ ] fishing.
- [ ] shopping.
- [ ] camping.

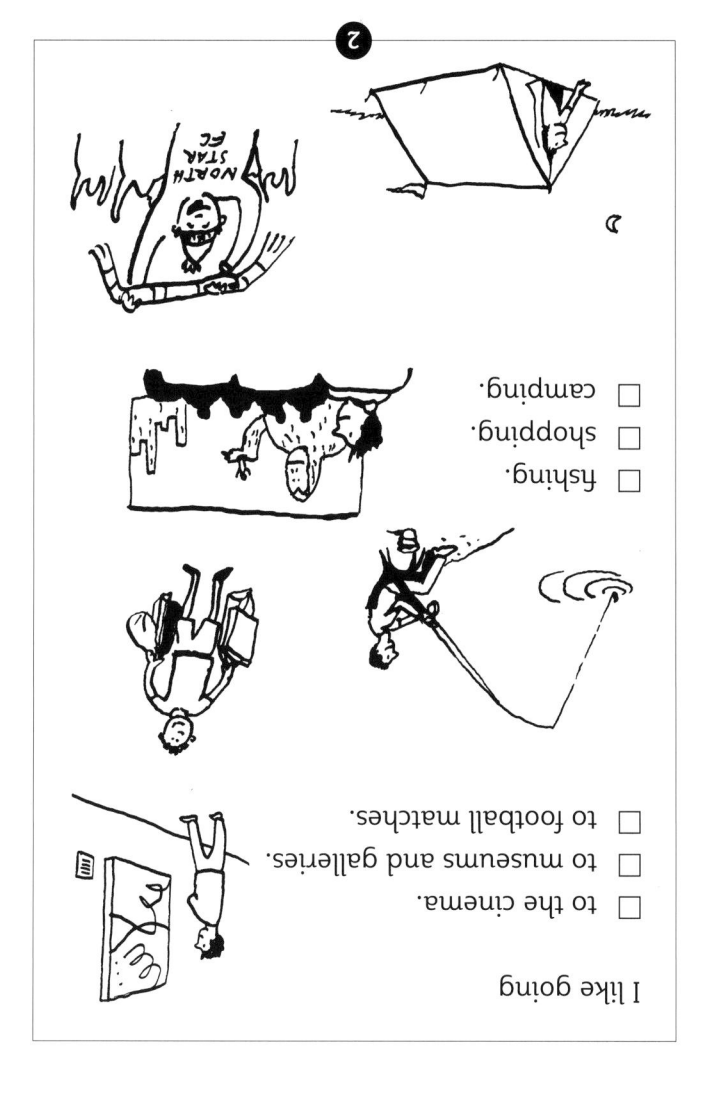

I like playing

- [ ] the piano.
- [ ] the trumpet.

- [ ] the guitar.
- [ ] the accordion.

- [ ] the drums.
- [ ] the keyboard.

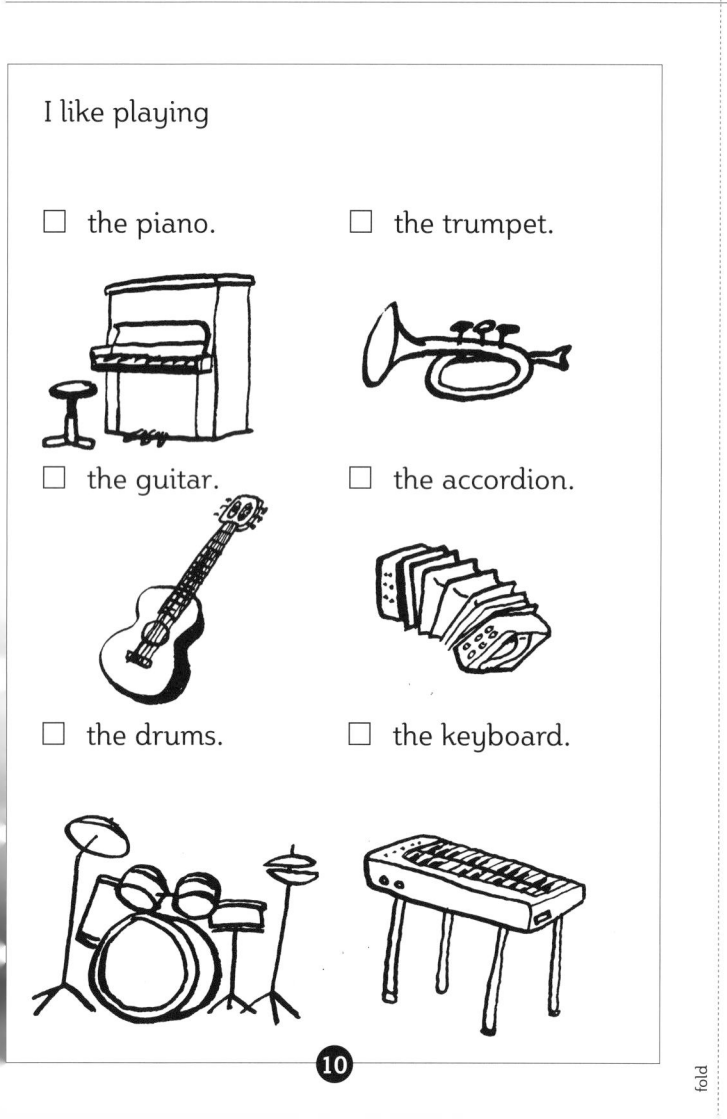

- [ ] I'd like to collect

....

and ....

My best friend is called

....

He/She likes

- [ ] the cinema
- [ ] watching TV
- [ ] sport
- [ ] music
- [ ] computers
- [ ] collecting ....
- [ ] playing .... ,

and ....

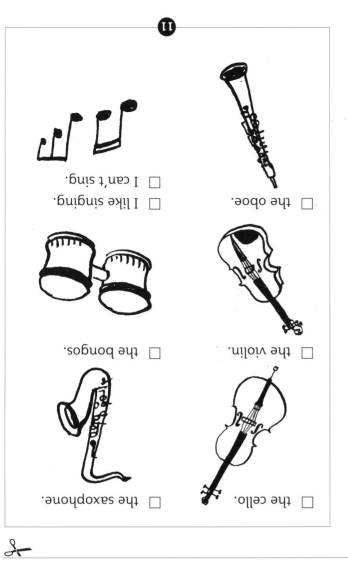

☐ I like singing. ☐ I can't sing.

☐ the oboe.

☐ the bongos. ☐ the violin.

☐ the saxophone. ☐ the cello.

and ....

☐ cuddly toys

☐ dolls

☐ spoons

☐ interesting stones

☐ fossils

☐ flags

☐ coins

☐ stamps

☐ I like collecting ...

My three favourite TV programmes are

1. .... ,
2. .... and
3. ....

Here is a photo of the star of my favourite TV show.

I like playing

☐ sports.
☐ a musical instrument.
☐ computer games.
☐ chess.
☐ cards.

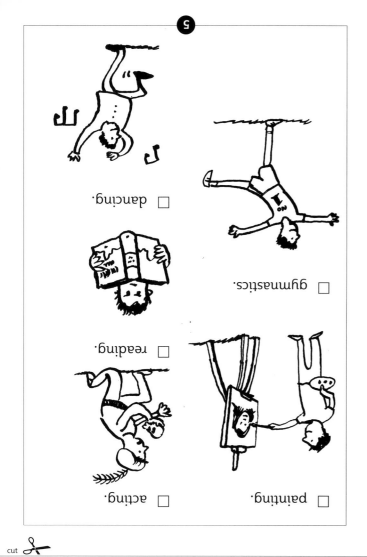

☐ painting.

☐ acting.

☐ reading.

☐ gymnastics.

☐ dancing.

fold

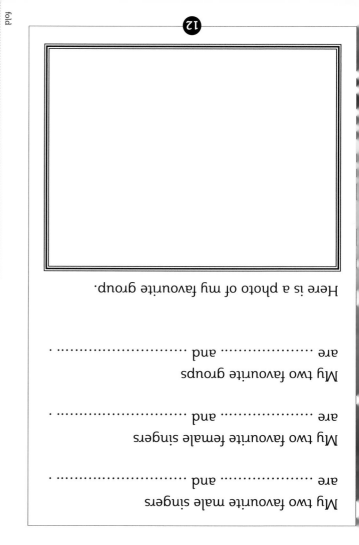

Here is a photo of my favourite group.

My two favourite male singers
are .... and ....

My two favourite female singers
are .... and ....

My two favourite groups
are .... and ....

---

cut ✂

I also like

☐ cooking.

☐ watching TV.

☐ skiing.

☐ listening to music.

I like

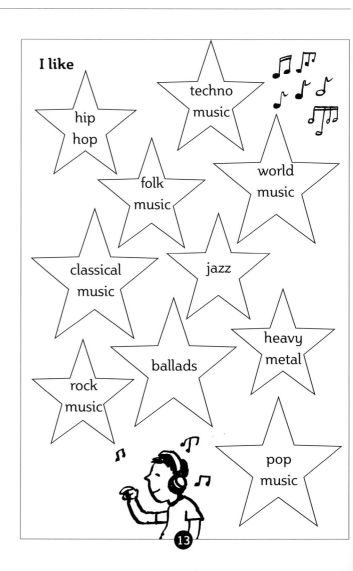

hip hop

techno music

folk music

world music

classical music

jazz

rock music

ballads

heavy metal

pop music

ANSWERS

Page 3
Fast foods: hamburgers, chips, hot dogs, pizza, salad
(NB although some of the other foods do not take a
long time to prepare, they are not the regular items
on takeaway/fast food menus.)

Page 4
butter, eggs, bananas, pasta, cheese, yoghurt, rice,
biscuits, nuts

Pages 6 & 7
1 knife, 2 spoon, 3 waiter, 4 chef, 5 fork, 6 table,
7 plate, 8 glass, 9 napkin, 10 bowl
(NB While most vegetarians eat these things, some
others, such as vegans, eat no animal products
whatsoever.)

Page 11
Students may need help filling in the answers to the
questionnaire about food.

Pages 12 & 13
Paella – Spain, burrito – Mexico, chicken curry – India,
spaghetti – Italy, roast beef – England, frankfurter
sausage – Germany, chop suey and rice – China, sushi
– Japan

Page 14

	F	ORK
KN	**I**	FE
	S	POON
C	**H**	EF
W	**A**	ITER
	N	APKIN
BREA	**D**	
	C	AKE
C	**H**	ICKEN
F	**I**	SH
CU	**P**	
GLA	**S**	S

Answer: FISH AND CHIPS

EXPLOITATION IDEAS

Who are the best cooks?
A lot of the best chefs in the world are male. Once
your students have filled in page 2 of their minibooks,
stop them and take a class vote to see how many of
them have nominated their father, brother or uncle. If
there are only a few, ask your students to think about
why the top chefs are men, and yet men don't do a lot
of cooking in the home.
Do any of the boys in class want to be chefs when
they are older? Ask:
How many of you can cook?
What can you cook?
What do you like cooking best?
If you have a few very keen cooks in the class they
could maybe bring in something they have prepared
to let everyone sample their efforts.

Fast foods
Depending on which country you live in there are
many example of 'fast foods' which you can eat
within moments of paying for them. What examples
can your students give of fast foods in your country?
Which ones have they tried in other countries?
Ask your students:
*Which do you like better – ..... (Name a fast food
restaurant) or ...... ? (Name some more traditional
authentic restaurants in your town.)*
Why do you prefer .... ?

Vegetarians
Give students a photocopied sheet. Instruct them to
go individually around the class interviewing about
five or six people each. After they have completed
their interviews they can give a short report. Here are
the questions for the sheet:
Are you a vegetarian?
If the answer is **yes**:
How long have you been a vegetarian?
*Are you a vegetarian because you don't like meat, or
because you want to be kind to animals?*
Are there other vegetarians in your family?
Do you eat fish?
*Which non-vegetarian foods do you sometimes think
you would like to eat?*

Do the restaurants in our town cook a lot of things for vegetarians?
If the answer is **no**:
Would you be very sad if I said: From now on you must be a vegetarian?
Is it cruel to animals to eat meat?
How many vegetarians do you know?
What vegetarian food do you like?
Is it healthy to be a vegetarian?

Restaurant role play

Use the minibook menu and the dialogue with the waiter/waitress on pages 8 and 9 to set up a restaurant role play. Once the students have worked with the menu, get them to create their own perfect menus for the class restaurant. One by one, they can read out their suggested menus in response to these prompts from you. Write them on the board and then the class can vote on whose 'restaurant' they would like to eat in most of all:
What are the 'starters'?
What are your main courses?
What are your side orders?
What are your desserts?

The perfect pizza

After your students have chosen what they want on their pizzas (page 15) get them to choose an original name for that pizza. Some of them may want to add ingredients which are not on page 15. This is perfectly possible.

The strangest thing I have ever eaten

If you have ever had a weird eating experience when abroad, share this with your students. If they have the language, they can all contribute to this discussion about strange things they have eaten on holiday. Describe the following ingredients for a dish to your students (you will have to translate some of the words):
The chopped heart, liver and lungs of a sheep, mixed with oatmeal, onion, spices and salt, and then cooked inside a cleaned sheep's stomach.
See if they can guess in which country people eat this. The answer is Scotland. It is a recipe for Scottish haggis. However, in modern times, a synthetic inedible 'skin' resembling a stomach is used and then discarded after the contents have been eaten. People do not use real sheep stomachs these days.

Drinks
cola
milk
tea
coffee

Desserts
ice cream
chocolate cake
cheese and biscuits

What would you like this evening?

I'd like .... to start.
Then I'd like .... for my main course, and I'd like .... with that.
For dessert I'd like .... ,
and I think I'd like .... to drink.

Side Orders
salad
chips
rice

Main Course
pizza
spaghetti with tomato sauce
hamburger
omelette

Starters
mushroom soup
chicken soup

Are you ready to order?

My favourite restaurant is called

....

When I go there, I usually have

....

I like it because
☐ it's friendly.
☐ the food is fantastic.
☐ my friends all go there.

This is a minibook about

Eating Out

by ....

cut ✂

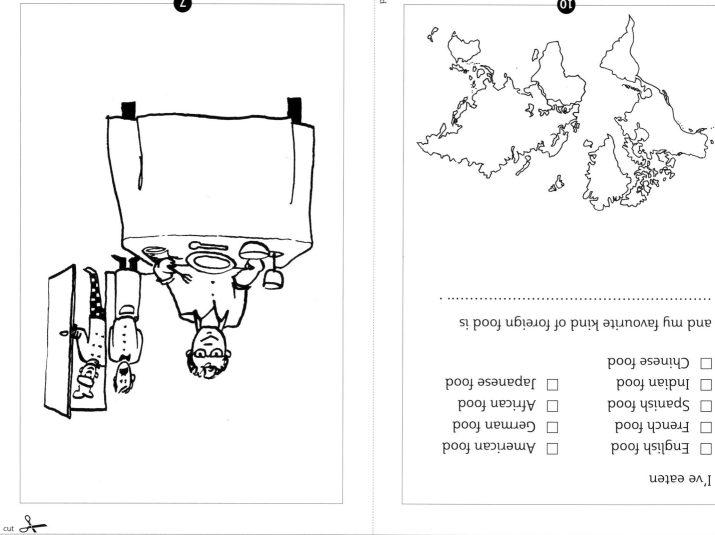

fold

I've eaten

- [ ] English food
- [ ] American food
- [ ] German food
- [ ] French food
- [ ] Spanish food
- [ ] Indian food
- [ ] Japanese food
- [ ] African food
- [ ] Chinese food

and my favourite kind of foreign food is

....

- [ ] I like eating out.
- [ ] I don't like eating out.

The best cook in our family is
- [ ] my dad.
- [ ] my mum.
- [ ] my grandma.
- [ ] my brother.
- [ ] my sister.
- [ ] my aunt.
- [ ] my uncle.

What's your favourite pizza?
Write the names of the things it has in it on the pizza below.

salami   ham
mushrooms   spinach
sardines   eggs
anchovies   onion
nuts   cheese
tomato   green peppers
pineapple   red peppers
olives

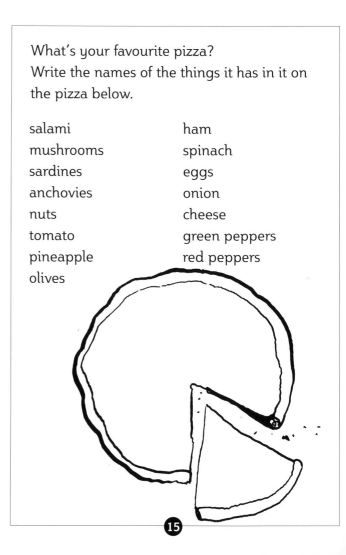

My favourite fruit is
....

My favourite vegetable is
....

My favourite fish is
....

My favourite meat is
....

The thing I can never eat is
....

I think the worst foreign dish is
....

The first time I tried it I was ...... years old.

My favourite foreign dish is
....

You can see all these in a restaurant.
What are they?

1. EKNFI ....

2. ONSPO ....

3. TRAWIE ....

4. FECH ....

5. KOFR ....

6. EBLAT ....

7. TEPAL ....

8. SAGLS ....

9. KNIPAN ....

10. LWOB ....

fold

There are lots of restaurants in England where you can buy this food. What is it?

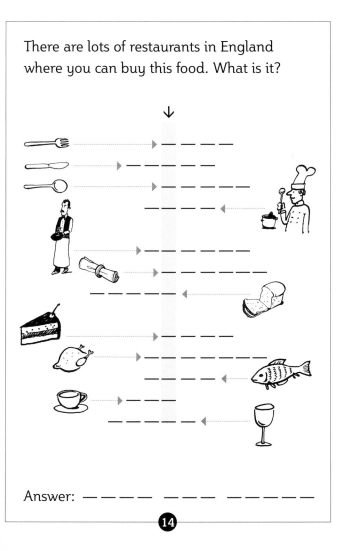

Answer: — — — — — — —

Which of these are 'fast foods'?

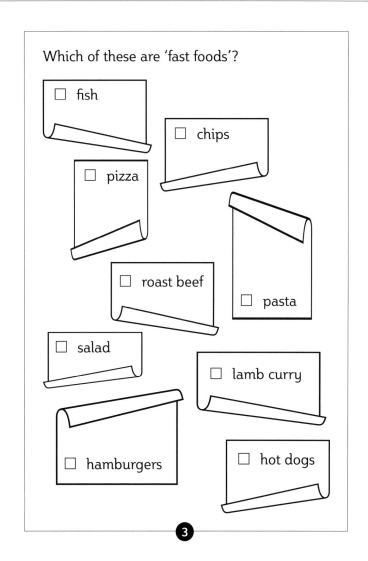

☐ fish

☐ chips

☐ pizza

☐ roast beef

☐ pasta

☐ salad

☐ lamb curry

☐ hamburgers

☐ hot dogs

☐ still water.

☐ sparkling water.

I like

My favourite drinks are:

☐ milk
☐ water
☐ coffee
☐ tea
☐ hot chocolate
☐ lemonade
☐ soft drinks
☐ orange juice

I'm not old enough to drink

☐ milkshakes.
☐ wine.
☐ tomato juice.
☐ beer.

Match the food to the country.

paella

burrito

chicken curry

spaghetti

roast beef

frankfurter sausage

chop suey and rice

sushi

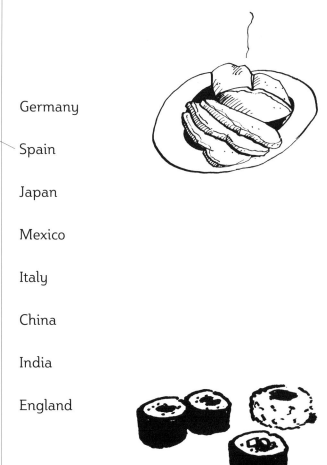

What can vegetarians eat?

☐ butter   ☐ yoghurt
☐ beef   ☐ ham
☐ eggs   ☐ lamb
☐ bananas   ☐ rice
☐ pasta   ☐ biscuits
☐ fish   ☐ hamburgers
☐ sausages   ☐ nuts
☐ cheese

Germany

Spain

Japan

Mexico

Italy

China

India

England

cut ✂

fold

ANSWERS

Pages 2 & 3
1 boat, 2 bicycle, 3 car, 4 plane, 5 helicopter, 6 motorbike, 7 train, 8 taxi, 9 bus, 10 lorry

Page 4

h	e	l	i	c	o	p	t	e	r
b	s	o	u	a	i	l	t	t	n
o	c	r	a	r	s	a	s	e	i
a	a	r	n	u	x	n	d	p	a
t	a	y	b	i	s	e	s	p	r
e	k	i	b	r	o	t	o	m	t
o	r	t	e	l	c	y	c	i	b

Page 5
Answer = suitcase and passport

Pages 8 & 9
1 – e. Yes, I'd like a ticket to Portsmouth, please., 2 – f. Yes, it is., 3 – c. Return, please., 4 – g. Yes, I am., 5 – a. Sorry, I've only got a £20 note., 6 – b. Thank you. When's the next train?, 7 – h. Thank you. Which platform?, 8 – d. Thank you very much. Goodbye.

Page 10
Milan, St Petersburg, Sydney, New York, Los Angeles and Frankfurt are not capital cities.
Italy, Greece, Malta, Ireland and Finland use euros.

Page 11
1 (b) London to Rome, 2 (b) Amsterdam to Beijing, 3 (b) Madrid to Tokyo, 4 (a) Sydney to Moscow, 5 (b) Chicago to San Francisco.

Pages 12 & 13
1 – f, 2 – b, 3 – g, 4 – a, 5 – c, 6 – d, 7 – e

EXPLOITATION IDEAS

Vocabulary practice
Before you begin the minibook of travelling, see how many words for means of transport that your students know. Write them on the board and teach any words that they may not already know, so that when they get to pages 2 and 3 they will be able to write in the correct words.

Buying a ticket: role play
Once your students have completed the dialogue at the railway ticket offlce on pages 8 & 9, they can role-play new situations where they are buying train tickets. Tell them to choose British destinations by looking at a map of Britain. Their journeys start in London. Make sure they vary the price of the tickets according to distance.

Geography quiz
Warn students that they are going to be doing a geography quiz in class, and that each of them should research three questions about the countries, rivers, and capital cities of the world by looking at their atlases at home. When it comes to doing the geography quiz, any student who manages to 'beat the class' by asking a question which no one can answer wins three points. Also, every student who answers a question correctly gets a point. Obviously you will have to judge whether the questions are suitable or not by vetting them in advance. Give a small prize to the winner. You could perhaps include a few time questions, which are good practice in telling the time as well as geography, e.g.
When it's four o'clock in New York, what time is it in Rome?
When it's half past six in London, what time is it in Los Angeles?
It is not expected that young children will know these answers. They can simply guess and see who has guessed closest to the correct answer. It also makes them aware of time difference around the world, as well as geographical distances.

Air travel

The vocabulary on minibook page 12 is quite difficult; however, if your students have travelled by air, they will have probably seen these signs in English in most places in the world. You may need to teach them the translations of these words before they actually tackle page 12. Ask them in the mother tongue what these terms mean. If they have not travelled by plane, they may not know the answers even in their own language.

The best seat on the plane

Wait until everyone has completed page 14 of their minibooks and then take votes and find out which is considered the best place to sit on the plane by most of the class. Ask:

Who has been on a plane?
Where did you go?
How long was the journey?
How many meals did you eat on the plane?
Did you sleep?
What did you do to pass the time?

Travel project

Do a travel project with your class. Get your students to make a large wall frieze showing where they have all been in the world. For each country or city named, get students to bring in a photo of themselves and a photo of the place. Each of the names of the cities can be done as artwork and stuck down at angles across the frieze, like labels on old-fashioned suitcases. On the frieze, there can also be a bar chart to show how many students have travelled by each of the various types of transport.

g. Yes, I am.

h. Thank you. Which platform?

f. Yes, it is.

e. Yes, I'd like a ticket to Portsmouth, please.

d. Thank you very much. Goodbye.

c. Return, please.

b. Thank you. When's the next train?

a. Sorry, I've only got a £20 note.

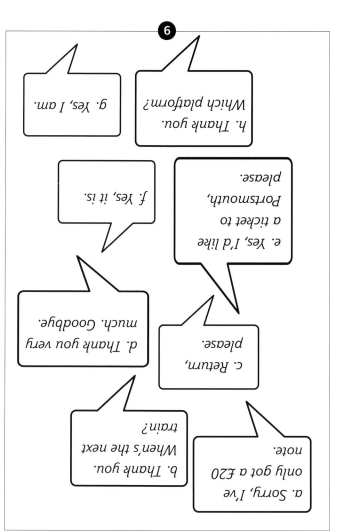

Buying a train ticket.
Find your answers on page 9. Write the answers in the spaces.

Ticket seller:

1. Can I help you?

e. Yes, I'd like a ticket to Portsmouth please.

2. That's a half fare, is it?

3. Single or return?

....

4. Are you returning on the same day?

....

5. The day return fare is £12.80.

....

6. That's OK. Here's your change – £7.20.

....

7. Three fifteen.

....

8. Platform seven.

....

© 2010 North Star ELT COPYKIT ENGLISH: Minibooks for Young Learners (ISBN 978-1-907584-02-2) www.northstarelt.co.uk

I have visited these countries:

....
....
....

I have visited these big cities:

....
....
....

I have travelled

☐ by car   ☐ by train
☐ by plane   ☐ by bus
☐ by boat   ☐ by helicopter

This is a minibook about
Travelling

by ....

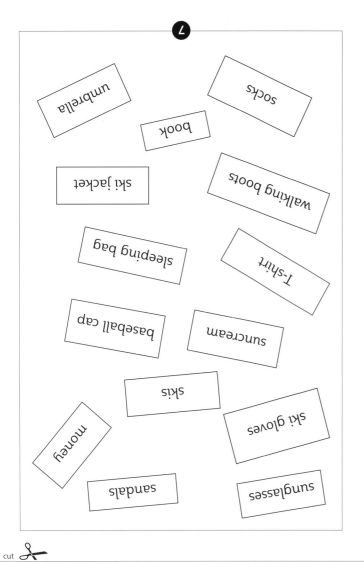

umbrella

socks

book

ski jacket

walking boots

sleeping bag

T-shirt

baseball cap

suncream

skis

money

ski gloves

sandals

sunglasses

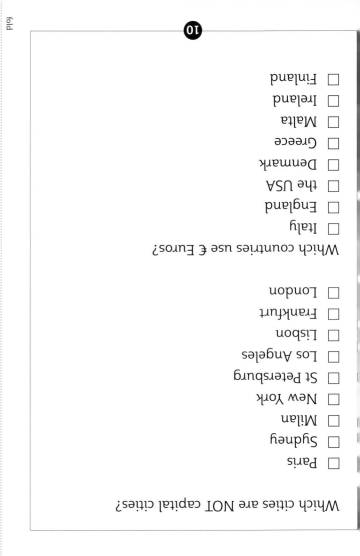

Which countries use € Euros?

☐ Finland
☐ Ireland
☐ Malta
☐ Greece
☐ Denmark
☐ the USA
☐ England
☐ Italy

Which cities are NOT capital cities?

☐ London
☐ Frankfurt
☐ Lisbon
☐ Los Angeles
☐ St Petersburg
☐ New York
☐ Milan
☐ Sydney
☐ Paris

Write the correct names under the pictures.

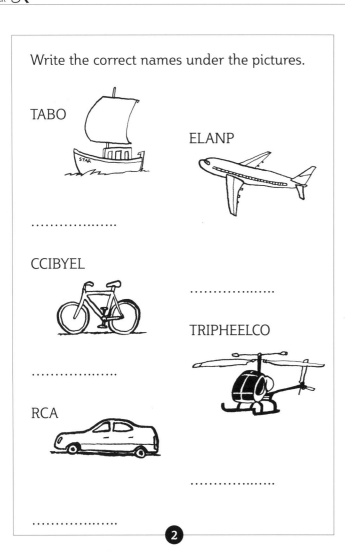

TABO

....

ELANP

....

CCIBYEL

....

TRIPHEELCO

....

RCA

....

When I'm travelling, I like to

☐ read a book.
☐ go to sleep.
☐ take photos.
☐ listen to music.
☐ play computer games.
☐ read a magazine.
☐ do puzzles.

Use an atlas to find which is further.

1. (a) London to Amsterdam
   or (b) London to Rome?

2. (a) Amsterdam to New York
   or (b) Amsterdam to Beijing?

3. (a) Madrid to Rio de Janeiro
   or (b) Madrid to Tokyo?

4. (a) Sydney to Moscow
   or (b) Frankfurt to Moscow?

5. (a) Chicago to New York
   or (b) Chicago to San Francisco?

Choose one of these holidays and choose a month, and pack the things you need from the list on page 7. Write the names of the things in the suitcase.

A camping holiday	in	September
A skiing holiday	in	February
A beach holiday	in	August

When I go on a plane, I like to sit

- ☐ next to a window.
- ☐ next to the aisle.
- ☐ near the front of the plane.
- ☐ near the back of the plane.
- ☐ near an exit door.
- ☐ near the toilet.
- ☐ next to my parents.
- ☐ behind my parents.

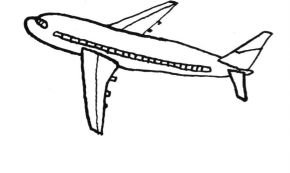

EKROOMBTI

SUB

....

RATIN

....

ROYLR

....

AXTI

....

....

(Draw your picture in the square above.)

This is a picture of them.

_____ ___ _____

Here are the two things you need when you travel. They are in the yellow squares in the grid on page 4:

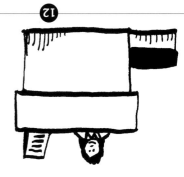

LONDON STANSTED

1   passport control
2   security
3   baggage reclaim
4   carousel
5   gate
6   check-in
7   runway

Match the names to the descriptions on page 13.

Find the words from pages 2 and 3. Colour the other letters yellow.

h	e	l	i	c	o	p	t	e	r
b	s	o	u	a	i	l	t	t	n
o	c	r	a	r	s	a	s	e	i
a	a	r	n	u	x	n	d	p	a
t	a	y	b	i	s	e	s	p	r
e	k	i	b	r	o	t	o	m	t
o	r	t	e	l	c	y	c	i	b

a. It moves and you take your bags from it.

b. They x-ray your hand luggage here.

c. You go here to get on the plane.

d. You show your tickets and leave your bag here.

e. The long road the plane uses before it goes into the sky.

f. The place where you show your passport.

g. The large room with the carousel.

ANSWERS

Pages 10 & 11
It's snowing in the Alps.
It's windy in Chicago.
It's raining in Stockholm.
It's cloudy in Barcelona.

Page 12
postcard, ice cream, suitcase, lifeguard, sunglasses, passport, surfboard, campsite

Page 14

N	C	A	U	S	T	R	I	A
O	M	A	N	P	A	R	T	J
R	E	C	N	A	R	F	A	B
W	X	Y		I	I	P	L	R
A	I	S	L	N	A	A	Y	A
Y	C	N	I	N	D	I	A	Z
D	O	Y	E	K	R	U	T	I
E	N	G	L	A	N	D	S	L

(Austria, France, India, Turkey, England, Norway, Mexico, Spain, Italy, Brazil, Japan)
The holiday destination is the CANARY ISLANDS.

Page 15
She is going to the United States of America.

EXPLOITATION IDEAS

School holidays
On minibook page 3 your students have to mark off all the days when there are school holidays. Point out that this is not a calendar for the year in which they now are; it is simply an example of a calendar. Ask your students to imagine that they can grant one more school holiday (just one day). Get them to give suggestions of when it might be and what or whom it might celebrate.

Holiday pastimes
Get your students to fill in the boxes on pages 4 and 5 but to suggest any other things that have been omitted from the list that they enjoy doing.

Packing your suitcase
Write the list of things on page 6 vertically down the left-hand side of the board. Read out the list and find out how many people put '1' by each item. Write all the students' names (or give them a number each if it is a large class) across the top of the board. Ask each student, one by one for their votes. They must call out the name of the item and then the number of points they gave it slowly so that you can add each number to the previous one that was given for each item. The item with the fewest votes is therefore the one that the class consider to be the most essential. There may of course be a bit of argument about the final outcome with people insisting that you can't go on holiday without something which has found itself at number four on the list.

Paradise Island

The exercise on pages 8 & 9 echoes the one at the beginning of the minibook, but it is there so that your students learn how to compromise and take each other's likes and dislikes into consideration. When everyone has agreed on their three activities, go round the class asking each pair how easy it was to reach a decision and if one had to change their first choice, what happened and what persuaded them to change. Did their friend put up a strong argument or did they just agree in order to have an easy life?

The weather

Write the following words on the board: a torch, sunglasses, a hat, gloves, an umbrella, a big scarf.
Now ask your students:
What do you need when it's snowing?
and get them to suggest appropriate things from the list.
Do the same with *raining, foggy, windy, sunny, frosty* and *stormy*.

Holiday song

Here is a simple holiday song to sing with the class. To hear the tune, type the following into an Internet search engine: 'Tune of the Quartermaster's Store'. On one of the many sites devoted to this song you will be able to hear the tune. However, here are some new words:
Verse 1:
There are kids, kids, camping in the park,
every day, every day.
There are kids, kids singing in the dark
on their happy holiday.
Chorus:
So let's have fun this holiday;
let's pack our bags and go away,
and let's all shout "Hip! Hip! Hooray!"
Verse 2:
There are kids, kids, swimming in the pool,
every day, every day.
There are kids, kids, keeping very cool
on our happy holiday. (+ chorus)
Verse 3:
There are kids, kids, cycling through the trees,
every day, every day.
There are kids, kids walking through the leaves
on our happy holiday. (+ chorus).

I want to	My friend wants to	So we'll both
play tennis		
go windsurfing		
go shopping		
stay in the hotel		
watch TV		
lie on the beach		
play a computer game		
go on a boat trip		

fold

You are on holiday on Paradise Island with your best friend.

Choose three things to do. Then ask your friend what he/she wants to do.

Remember, you must both agree on only three things.

© 2010 North Star ELI COPYKIT ENGLISH: Minibooks for Young Learners (ISBN 978-1-907584-02-2) www.northstarelt.co.uk

The three places I want to go to on my dream holiday are:

1. ....
because I love ....
....
....

2. ....
because I love ....
....
....

3. ....
because I love ....
....
....

This is a minibook about

Holidays

by ....

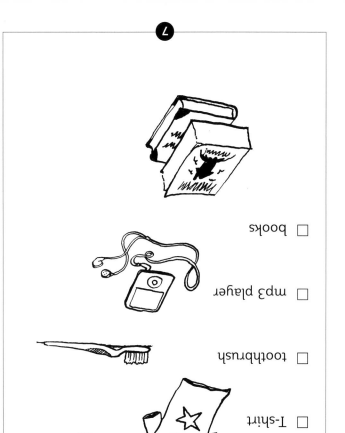

- ☐ trainers
- ☐ T-shirt
- ☐ toothbrush
- ☐ mp3 player
- ☐ books

Holiday weather

Look at the weather symbol and write it in the first half of the sentence. Then work out the anagrams to find the names of the places.

1. It's s............ in the ....
   Alps

2. It's w............ in ....
   ....

I like
- ☐ relaxing holidays.
- ☐ activity holidays.
- ☐ to stay at home.
- ☐ to travel.

Where is Tessa going on her holiday?

She is going to

....

....

....

We have school holidays on these days.
(Circle them in red)

JANUARY						
M	T	W	T	F	S	S
		01	02	03	04	05
06	07	08	09	10	11	12
13	14	15	16	17	18	19
20	21	22	23	24	25	26
27	28	29	30	31		

FEBRUARY						
M	T	W	T	F	S	S
					01	02
03	04	05	06	07	08	09
10	11	12	13	14	15	16
17	18	19	20	21	22	23
24	25	26	27	28		

MARCH						
M	T	W	T	F	S	S
					01	02
03	04	05	06	07	08	09
10	11	12	13	14	15	16
17	18	19	20	21	22	23
24	25	26	27	28	29	30
31						

APRIL						
M	T	W	T	F	S	S
	01	02	03	04	05	06
07	08	09	10	11	12	13
14	15	16	17	18	19	20
21	22	23	24	25	26	27
28	29	30				

MAY						
M	T	W	T	F	S	S
			01	02	03	04
05	06	07	08	09	10	11
12	13	14	15	16	17	18
19	20	21	22	23	24	25
26	27	28	29	30	31	

JUNE						
M	T	W	T	F	S	S
						01
02	03	04	05	06	07	08
09	10	11	12	13	14	15
16	17	18	19	20	21	22
23	24	25	26	27	28	29
30						

JULY						
M	T	W	T	F	S	S
	01	02	03	04	05	06
07	08	09	10	11	12	13
14	15	16	17	18	19	20
21	22	23	24	25	26	27
28	29	30	31			

AUGUST						
M	T	W	T	F	S	S
				01	02	
04	05	06	07	08	09	
11	12	13	14	15	16	
18	19	20	21	22	23	
25	26	27	28	29	30	31

SEPTEMBER						
M	T	W	T	F	S	S
01	02	03	04	05		
06	07	08	09	10	11	12
13	14	15	16	17	18	19
20	21	22	23	24	25	26
27	28	29	30			

OCTOBER						
M	T	W	T	F	S	S
	01	02	03	04	05	
06	07	08	09	10	11	
13	14	15	16	17	18	
20	21	22	23	24	25	26
27	28	29	30	31		

NOVEMBER						
M	T	W	T	F	S	S
				01	02	
03	04	05	06	07	08	09
10	11	12	13	14	15	16
17	18	19	20	21	22	23
24	25	26	27	28	29	30

DECEMBER						
M	T	W	T	F	S	S
01	02	03	04			
05	06	07	08	09	10	11
12	13	14	15	16	17	18
19	20	21	22	23	24	25
26	27	28	29	30	31	

Find eleven countries in the grid: **Austria,**
France, India, Turkey, England, Norway,
Mexico, Spain, Italy, Brazil, Japan.
Colour all the other squares yellow.

A	I	R	T	S	U	A	C	N
O	M	A	N	P	A	R	T	J
R	E	C	N	A	R	F	A	B
W	X	Y	I	I	P	L	R	
A	I	S	L	N	A	Y	A	
Y	C	N	I	N	D	I	A	Z
D	O	Y	K	R	U	I	I	
E	N	G	L	A	N	D	S	L

Write the letters in the yellow squares here.
The white square is the space between two
words. It's a famous holiday place.

‗ ‗ ‗ ‗ ‗ ‗ □ ‗ ‗ ‗ ‗

These are the things people take on their
holidays.
Put a '1' by the most important thing, a '2'
by the next important thing, etc.

☐ sunglasses

☐ money

☐ mobile phone

☐ pyjamas

☐ camera

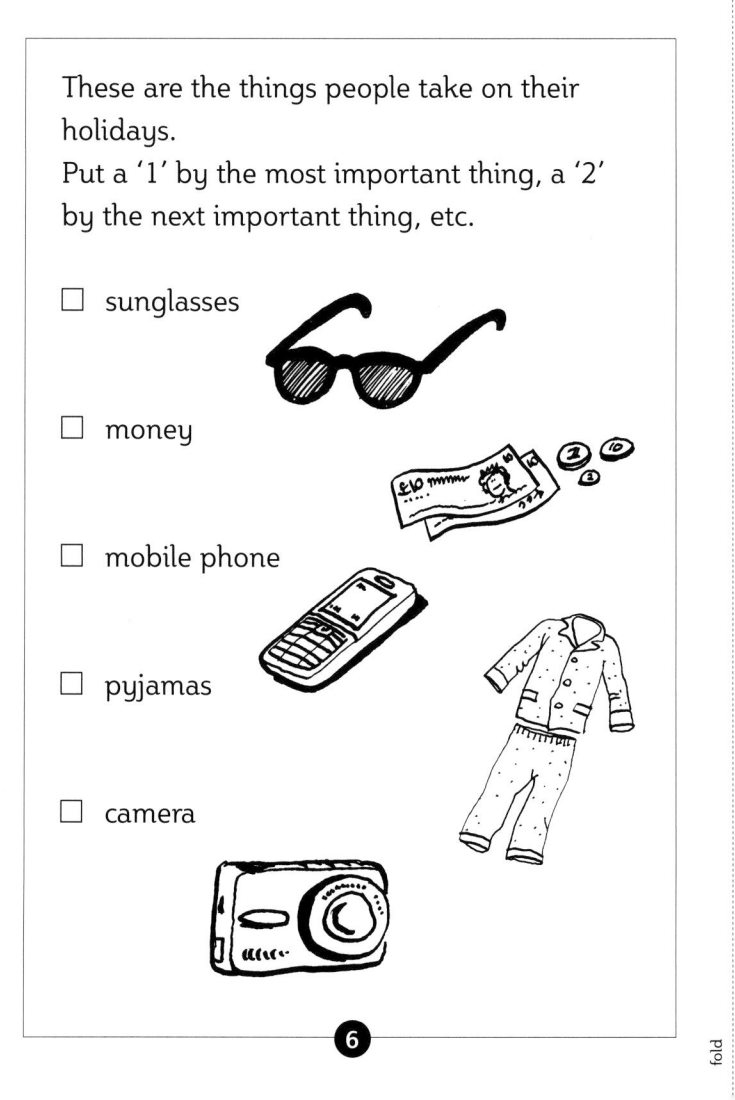

3. It's r..................... in
....

4. It's c..................... in
....

Page 5

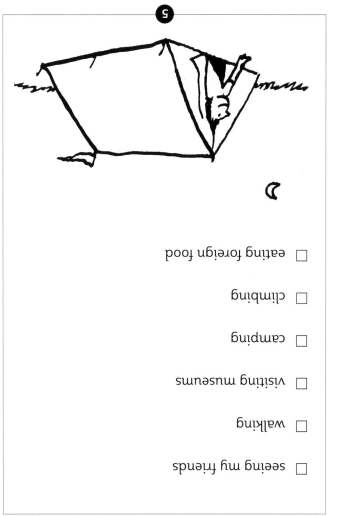

- [ ] seeing my friends
- [ ] walking
- [ ] visiting museums
- [ ] camping
- [ ] climbing
- [ ] eating foreign food

Page 12

Find the two parts of the words, then write them under the pictures. You can see these things on your holiday.

glasses	post
port	ice
board	suit
guard	life
site	sun
card	pass
cream	surf
case	camp

Page 4

These are the things I like doing on my holidays:

- [ ] sunbathing
- [ ] playing volleyball
- [ ] sailing
- [ ] swimming
- [ ] skiing
- [ ] sleeping

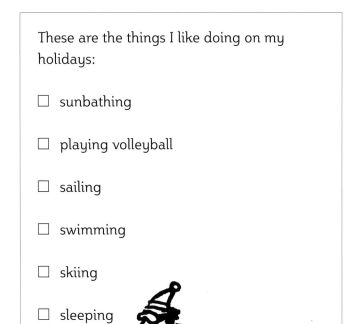

Page 13

postcard

....

....

....

....

cut

ANSWERS

Page 4

1 Beethoven, 2 *The Barber of Seville*, 3 Mick Jagger,
4 Trumpet, 5 Kylie Minogue, 6 Coldplay, 7 Placido
Domingo, 8 Tango, 9 *Swan Lake*, 10 *Chasing Cars*

Page 6

1 *God Save the Queen*, 2 *Yesterday*, 3 *The Phantom of
the Opera*, 4 *Thank you for the music*, 5 hymns, 6 loud,
7 jazz singers

Page 11

1. Ten green bottles, standing on a wall
2. I'm singing in the rain
3. We all live in a yellow submarine
4. I'd like to teach the world to sing
5. Cecilia, you're breaking my heart
6. I see trees that are green, red roses too
7. The hills are alive with the sound of music
8. What about sunrise? What about rain?

Pages 12 and 13

1 trombone, 2 cello, 3 clarinet, 4 cymbals

Page 14

The answers (i.e., *north, south, east* or *west*) will depend
on where you are.
The correct choices for the rest of the song are: *call
'home', cool,* and *me.*

Page 15

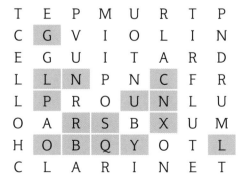

EXPLOITATION IDEAS

Talking about music

Pages 2 and 3 are a warm-up exercise for talking
about music. Once everyone has filled in their correct
answers, you can ask around the class to find out who
is and who isn't musical. Explain that they simply have
to read out the correct complete sentence that applies
to them. Some students may be able to play more
than one instrument, so they can make a list using
and. You may wish to reveal which option applies to
you as well.

Names of instruments

To practise the names of the various instruments it is
a good idea to sing the popular song, *The Music Man.*
You can find the lyrics on the Internet just by typing in
the words *Music Man lyrics* on your browser. There
are also excellent little films on YouTube of singers
performing this song with children.
Your students might be able to invent the sounds and
actions for instruments other than those mentioned in
the song.

Music survey

Following the 'Music and Musicians' section and also
the 'Big Music Quiz', ask each student to make up just
one music question which he/she can ask the rest of
the class. When everyone has a music question, you
can have a big class music quiz.

Separate the class into two teams and then, one by
one, the members of each team can put their question
to the opposing team.

Note that the suffix –*ist* usually signifies someone
who plays that instrument *(violinist, clarinetist,
saxophonist, guitarist, pianist (not pianoist), cellist (not
celloist), flautist (not flutist) etc.).* However, there are
some exceptions, e.g. *drummer, keyboard player, horn
player* and *trumpeter.*

Famous songs

The songs whose lines appear on page 11 are by the following artists:

1 (*Traditional*), 2 Gene Kelly, 3 The Beatles, 4 The New Seekers, 5 Simon and Garfunkel, 6 Louis Armstrong, 7 Julie Andrews, 8 Michael Jackson.

Once again, encourage your students to bring lines (in English of course) from popular songs, and see if anyone else in the class can guess where they come from. Of course, caution should be used when dealing with song lyrics, as they are sometimes ungrammatical and, worse, rude or offensive.

Class orchestra

If there are quite a few musicians in the class, they could bring in some of their instruments to create a little class orchestra. Hopefully they could perform an English song for the class to sing. The vocabulary (*woodwind, percussion*, etc) may be a bit advanced, but the children have probably studied the basic facts about the orchestra in their own language.

Change the lyrics

You may want to try using simple song tunes and nursery rhymes with new English lyrics, especially action songs and games. The following can also be sung to the tune of *Twinkle, Twinkle Little Star* and has actions:

Stand up straight, be very tall
Now sit down; be very small
Twist your body, turn around,
Bend right over, touch the ground,
Touch your ears and touch your knee
And then sit down quietly.

Sit right down upon your heel
Stretch one leg (How does that feel?)
Touch your shoulders, touch your nose,
Bend right over, touch your toes,
Touch your ears and touch your knee
And then sit down quietly.

My pop group

My pop group will be called

....

The group will have
- ☐ two people in it.
- ☐ three people in it.
- ☐ four people in it.
- ☐ five people in it.

Our first single will be called

....

I will be
- ☐ the singer.
- ☐ the guitarist.
- ☐ the drummer.
- ☐ the violinist.
- ☐ the keyboard player.
- ☐ the trumpet player.

We will play
- ☐ happy songs.
- ☐ love songs.
- ☐ loud rock music.
- ☐ folk music.
- ☐ electronic music.

My solo career

My first single will be called:

....

It will be a
- ☐ pop song.
- ☐ heavy metal song.
- ☐ love song.
- ☐ folk song.
- ☐ rap.

I will sing
- ☐ in big concert stadiums.
- ☐ in small clubs.
- ☐ at big pop festivals.
- ☐ on the street and the underground.
- ☐ on TV.

My favourite music

My favourite pop song is

....

My three favourite female singers are

1 ....

2 ....

3 ....

My three favourite male singers are

1 ....

2 ....

3 ....

My three favourite groups are

1 ....

2 ....

3 ....

My favourite musical is

....

My favourite album is

....

The next album I want to buy is

....

by ....

© 2010 North Star ELI COPYKIT ENGLISH: Minibooks for Young Learners (ISBN 978-1-907584-02-2) www.northstarelt.co.uk

This is a minibook about

Music

by ....

7. Billie Holiday and Ella Fitzgerald were famous
□ opera singers.
□ folk singers.
□ jazz singers.

6. Heavy metal music is
□ quiet.
□ romantic.
□ loud.

5. Church songs are called
□ prayers.
□ choirs.
□ hymns.

4. Abba sang a song called
□ Do you like music?
□ I love music.
□ Thank you for the music.

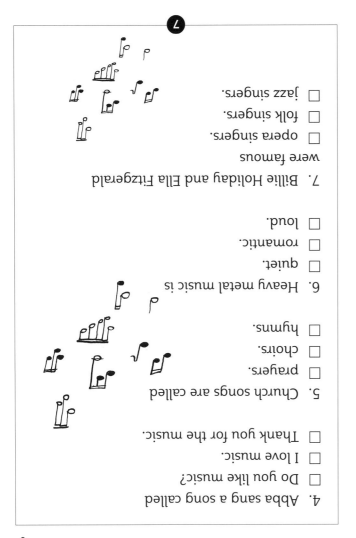

When I'm famous

I'll buy a house in
□ the Caribbean.
□ London.
□ the South of France.
□ New York.
□ Los Angeles.

And I will have lots of
□ dogs,
□ horses,
□ cars,
□ money,

□ but there will be no photos of me in the newspapers.
□ and there will be lots of photos of me in the newspapers.

This will be my autograph

Are you musical?
Tick ✓ one of the 4 boxes. (Choose an instrument from Page 3.)

□ I can play the

.... and I can sing.

□ I can play the

.... but I can't sing.

□ I can't play an instrument but I can sing.

□ I can't play and instrument and I can't sing.

Musical instrument word search
Find the ten musical instruments

T	E	P	M	U	R	T	P
C	G	V	I	O	L	I	N
E	G	U	I	T	A	R	D
L	L	N	P	N	C	F	R
L	P	R	O	U	N	L	U
O	A	R	S	B	X	U	M
H	O	B	Q	Y	O	T	L
C	L	A	R	I	N	E	T

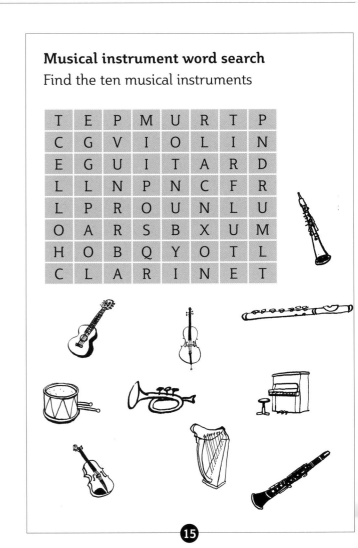

Famous songs

What are the correct song lines?

1. standing wall on Ten bottles a green
2. in I'm the rain singing
3. submarine We a in live all yellow
4. sing like to I'd world the teach to
5. my breaking heart Cecilia you're
6. that are roses too green I trees see red
7. sound are the of with music The alive hills
8. What rain? about What sunrise? about

THE BIG MUSIC QUIZ

1. The national anthem of Great Britain is called
   - ☐ *Land of Hope and Glory.*
   - ☐ *Rule Britannia.*
   - ☐ *God Save the Queen.*

2. The Beatles wrote a song called
   - ☐ *Yesterday.*
   - ☐ *Today.*
   - ☐ *Tomorrow.*

3. Andrew Lloyd Webber wrote a musical called
   - ☐ *The Sound of Music.*
   - ☐ *The Phantom of the Opera.*
   - ☐ *Mamma Mia.*

My own song

Choose the right words to write this song then sing it to the tune of
Twinkle, Twinkle, Little Star

- ☐ North
- ☐ South of Moscow,
- ☐ East
- ☐ West

- ☐ north
- ☐ south of Rome,
- ☐ east
- ☐ west

there's a place that I
- ☐ don't know.
- ☐ call 'home'.
- ☐ come from.

It is such a special school,
all the teachers are so
- ☐ nice.
- ☐ rude.
- ☐ cool.

It's the place I want to be. All my friends
agree with
- ☐ me.
- ☐ this.
- ☐ that.

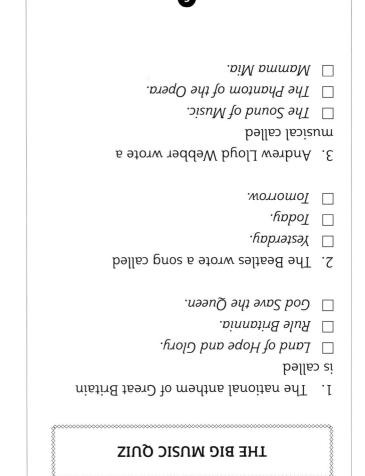

piano   accordion   harp

guitar   keyboard   saxophone

drum   cello   flute

trombone   violin   clarinet

trumpet   oboe

Kylie Minogue

Chasing Cars

The Barber of Seville

Beethoven

Placido Domingo

Tango

Coldplay

Trumpet

Mick Jagger

Swan Lake

---

cut ✂

The conductor tells the different parts of the orchestra when they must play.

There are 4 parts in an orchestra:

1. BRASS

TRUMPET

The trumpet is a brass instrument. Write the name of another brass instrument here: ....

2. STRING

VIOLIN

The violin is a string instrument. Write the name of another string instrument here: ....

Music and musicians

Look at page 5 and find the answers.

1. A classical composer
....

2. An opera
....

3. A rock star (male)
....

4. A musical instrument
....

5. A pop singer (female)
....

6. A pop group
....

7. An opera singer
....

8. A dance
....

9. A ballet
....

10. A love song
....

---

3. WOODWIND

FLUTE

The flute is a woodwind instrument. Write the name of another woodwind instrument here:
....

4. PERCUSSION

DRUM

The drum is a percussion instrument. Write the name of another percussion instrument here: ....

 CLARINET

 TROMBONE

 CELLO

 CYMBALS